Mr Greathead's Lifeboats

Adrian G. Osler

© Tyne and Wear Museums Service, 1990
Published by Tyne and Wear Museums Service, Blandford House, Blandford Square,
Newcastle upon Tyne.

Photography: Les Golding, Tyne and Wear Museums Service.
Design: Joan Nicklin and Susan McDonald, Newcastle City Council Graphics
Department.
Typeset by Keyline, Newcastle upon Tyne.
Printed by E. F. Peterson and Son, South Shields.

ISBN 0 905974 47 6

Author's Acknowledgements

Almost all research takes as its starting point already published works, and this present study is no exception. On a national level the author is particularly indebted to the meticulous studies of early lifeboats by the late Grahame Farr; locally, the detailed service-records of Tyneside lifesaving agencies prepared by Boswell Whitaker were also helpful.

In the museum world particular thanks go to Simon Stephens of the National Maritime Museum, not only for drawing attention to material which might otherwise have gone unnoticed, but also for his unselfish assistance and encouragement along the way. The facilities provided by the National Maritime Museum itself greatly helped to enhance the contents of this book.

As always, the services provided by the region's libraries have played a vital part, with especial help from the South Shield's Library, Miss Norwell of Newcastle Literary and Philosophical Society's Library, and Frank Manders and his ever patient colleagues in Newcastle Central Library. Similarly, there would have been little flesh on the bare bones of this study without the information gained from archival material. The opportunity provided by Dr. Colin Shrimpton of the Duke of Northumberland's Estate Office, Alnwick Castle, led the way. Two collections held by the Northumberland County Record Office (Browne-Swinburne collection and the Crewe Trustees collection), proved to be key elements in understanding Greathead's approach to lifeboat building, and the Admiralty collections at the Public Record Office yielded important insights into his early life. Abroad, staff of museums and record offices in Sweden and Denmark carried out searches on the author's behalf. Too numerous to mention are the many individuals and institutions who have answered enquiries concerning Greathead-built lifeboats, but particular thanks go to museum colleagues Arthur Credland, Martin Warren, Charles Lewis and Harry Fancy. A number of other friends and colleagues have, wittingly or unwittingly, also provided material which became grist to the Greathead mill.

Since publication is the desired endpoint to research there is a very real expression of gratitude to all those who have made the publication of this book possible, but especially to my Museum Service colleagues: Mel Twelves, for commercial support; Les Golding, for skilful in-house photography; Bob Elsey, for conserving and discussing with me the lifeboat models; Barbara Mohan and Monica Newcombe for indefatigable typing; together with Joan Nicklin and Sue McDonald of Newcastle City Graphics Department for bringing visual order to a complex project; and to Ian Whitehead and my wife for helping steer this small craft through the final tricky stages of its passage.

Finally, acknowledgement must be made to that rich cast of eighteenth century characters – from unknown carpenters to noble Dukes – who provided the real life drama behind this story of "Mr. Greathead's Life Boats".

Adrian G. Osler
January 1990

Sponsors' Foreword

Anyone who has any involvement with the sea has every reason to applaud and support the development of the lifeboat and the RNLI. Even if they never have reason to call upon its services, the knowledge that such a service exists for every seafaring person, operated by individuals willing to risk their lives in the worst possible weather conditions, is a reassuring thought.

The Occidental Consortium and Press Offshore are therefore delighted to offer their support to this book and to draw attention to others, who are perhaps not so closely involved with the sea and the dangers it can present, how important the invention of the Lifeboat was and what an excellent opportunity this book offers to read of its history and development.

John Brading,
Chairman and C.E.O.
Occidental Petroleum (Caledonia) Ltd.

Dennis Clark, O.B.E.
Chairman,
Press Offshore Ltd.

THE OCCIDENTAL CONSORTIUM

Press Offshore

Foreword

To claim priority of invention for a particular technical innovation, or a first in any field of humanitarian endeavour, is always risky for the attentions of counter-claimants and detractors are almost sure to follow. So the claims of an individual, Henry Greathead, to have been the inventor of the *Life-Boat*, and the more general assertion by the town of South Shields that it was the birthplace of lifeboat services (1789-90), almost inevitably resulted in longstanding controversy.

It is probably unrealistic to suggest that now, two centuries later, these matters can be definitively resolved. But the occasion of the bicentenary of this world-famous lifeboat's first use provides a prime opportunity for a re-examination of the facts and myths surrounding the origin of the Shields lifeboat. That this task should be carried out by the Tyne and Wear Museums Service is most appropriate, since it is the proud holder of the legendary Willie Wouldhave's experimental lifeboat model of 1789, and much historic lifeboat material besides. Additionally, through nationwide museum contacts it has proved possible for the museums service to locate many other relevant artefacts whilst, at the same time, the discovery of previously unexamined archival material (in various collections) has added a new dimension to the lifeboat story.

The story itself has proved to be a rich and complex one, the elucidation of which well illustrates the advantages of a museum approach – by which apparently unrelated sources may be drawn together. It is also a timely reminder that no aspect of our heritage can be 'written in tablets of stone', but must always remain open to new lines of research and interpretation. Perhaps, more philosophically, this little story also raises the question of how far apart the societies and motives of 1790 and 1990 really are.

Nevertheless, whatever the real intentions and actions of the men behind the establishment of the first Shields lifeboat may have been, all who have used the sea would surely agree with the sentiment behind a rhetorical question which was posed by the *Newcastle Courant* at that time, "What reward is sufficient for the man who saves the life of a fellow creature?"

John Thompson
Director of Museums and
Art Galleries
Tyne and Wear Museums Service

Councillor Barney Rice, J.P.
Chairman
Tyne and Wear Museums Service
Joint Committee

Contents

Introduction

The story of the origin of the Shields lifeboat is one which has been retold with varying degrees of embellishment and partisanship for nearly two hundred years. At its most simplistic and commonplace the story is reduced to a unique, eureka-like scenario in which the lifeboat is invented by an eccentric Shields genius, William Wouldhave, with an added adverserial twist by which he is robbed of his just rewards and fame by the boatbuilder Henry Greathead. Similarly, the Shields lifeboat itself becomes a craft of incomparable performance whose (genuinely magnificent) local lifesaving record reflected poorly upon the neglectful world which lay beyond the environs of Shields. Indeed, there are elements of truth in such commonly held views but, even after two centuries, a review of the surviving evidence indicates that a rather different and much more complex pattern of events actually lay behind the origin of, and subsequent controversies over, the "Life-Boat" at South Shields.

Excepting for a single commodity, coal, there is little reason to believe that by the end of the eighteenth century the river Tyne would have carried more shipping than any other provincial river of comparable size. But Britain's developing, energy-dependent domestic and industrial regimes were literally fuelling themselves on an increased demand for that river basin's staple product. By the 1780s, the river's own registered shipping tonnage (of around 106,000 tons)[1] was second only to that of London's, whilst ship clearances from the river in 1787 were reported to have reached almost 5,000, of which 4,400 were assigned to the coastal trade.[2]

All such ship movements took place through an unimproved and constricted river entrance, which is best described by a master-mariner of the day:[3]

> *"...the entrance into the harbour is very narrow, with dangerous rocks on one side, and a steep sand bank on the other, with a hard shoal bar a-cros, where the waves of the sea frequently run very high..."*

Though a seaman of the day would readily have grasped the realities behind those plain words of William Hutchinson it is not easy for us to visualise what they conveyed. At best a difficult approach from the sea, requiring the acknowledged skills of the "Pilots of Tinmouth Haven", and at worst, an unmarked maelstrom of house-high, toppling waves, driving onshore before winter's easterly gales. Any mistake, or misfortune, could lead a vessel to break its back on "the hard shoal bar", splinter itself open on the "dangerous rocks", or drive irretrievably into the ship-smashing surf of the "steep sand bank". In an era when overall shipping losses are estimated to have run at around 4% per annum perhaps the surprise is not so much in the number of wrecks at such a busy and difficult harbour-mouth but, as indicated by the admittedly imperfect contemporary accounts, in the apparently low frequency with which a ship and its complement were totally lost there.

1. The mouth of the Tyne (1a – above) and its approaches (1b – opposite), from a contemporary coasting chart by Laurie and Whittle of London, 1794.
2. (Inset) Two-masted brig or snow-rigged vessels (like the *Adventure*) were fast becoming the main carriers in the Coal Trade – though few such workaday craft carried figureheads.

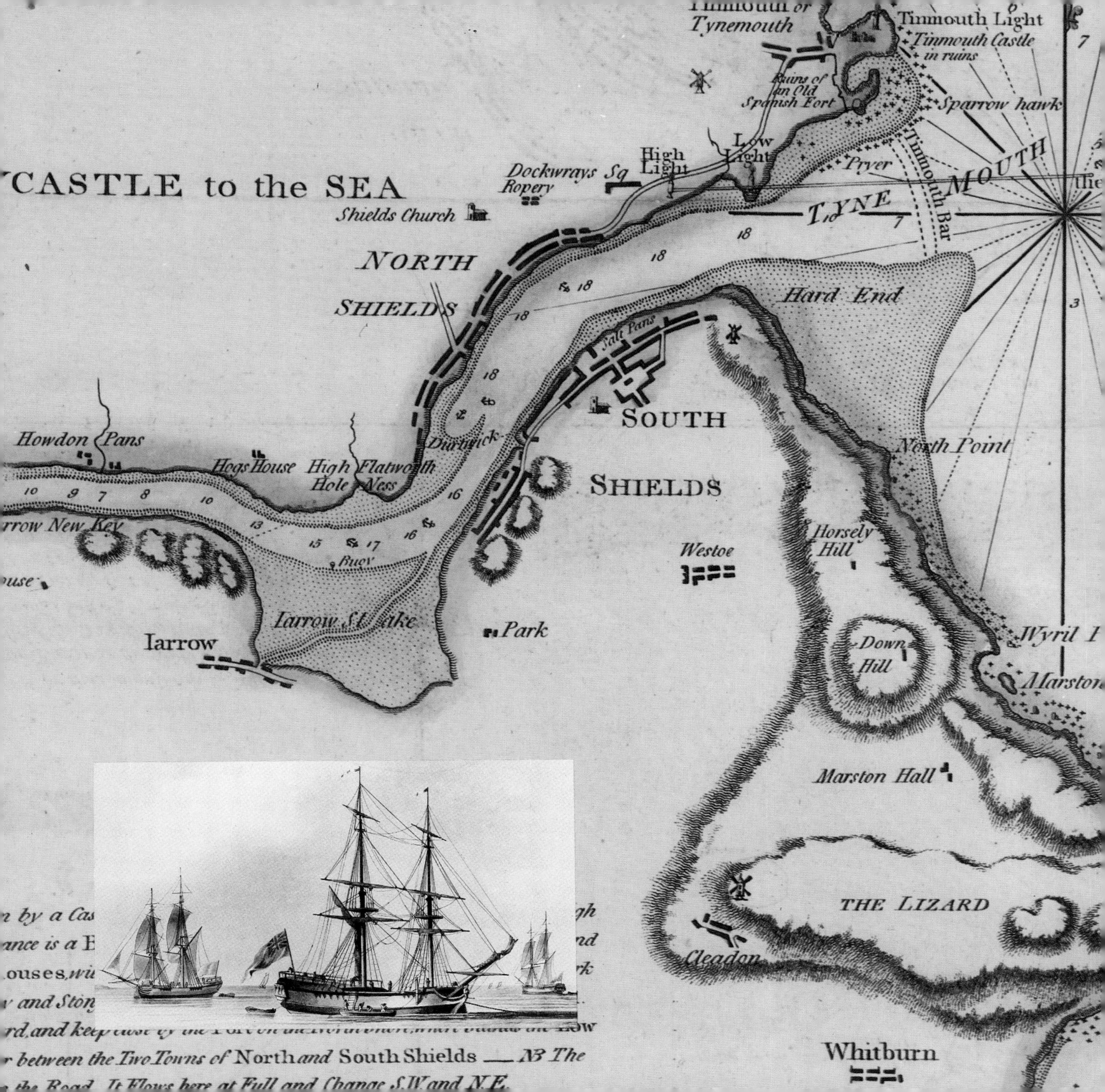

CASTLE to the SEA

Tinmouth or Tynemouth

Tinmouth Light

Tinmouth Castle in ruins

Ruins of an Old Spanish Fort

Sparrow hawk

Dockwrays Sq

High Light

Low Light

Pryer

Tinmouth Bar

TYNE MOUTH

Shields Church

NORTH SHIELDS

18

18

18

18

18

7

Hard End

Salt Pans

SOUTH SHIELDS

North Point

Howdon Pans

Hogs House

High Hole

Flatworth Ness

Darwick

10   9   7   8

10

13

15   17   16

Buoy

16

Westoe

Horsely Hill

rrow New Key

house

Iarrow Slake

Park

Iarrow

Down Hill

Wyril I

Marston

Marston Hall

THE LIZARD

Cleadon

Whitburn

n by a Cas
ance is a E
ouses, wi
v and Ston
rd, and keep clos
r between the Two Towns of North and South Shields ____ N3 The
the Road. It Flows here at Full and Change S.W and N.E.

3. In onshore gales – with spars struck, sails deep-reefed and decks awash – even the best of brigs could be driven relentlessly downwind, towards destruction.

4. A century after the loss of the *Adventure* the Tyne entrance still claimed sailing ships. But its Shields-type lifeboats were now supplemented by an R.N.L.I. self-righter.

This may well help to explain the unusual prominence given both at the time, and later, to the particular loss of the *Adventure*, of Newcastle, on the rivermouth Herd Sands below South Shields in March 1789 – a reaction analogous to our present day indifference to the cumulative toll of minor road accidents when compared with the immediate public and media reaction which follows the occasional tragedy of a local, motorway 'pile-up'. Although the *Adventure's* owners were Newcastle-based, and she was a constant trader to that port, it would have been surprising had they promoted further action, their concerns more likely being centred on the results than the dangers of the trade. In any event, matters of navigational safety and maritime relief or reward would have been considered the province of Newcastle's long-established Trinity House. Within weeks of the *Adventure's* loss, it was to the Trinity House secretary that a South Shields shipowner addressed his ideas for the provision of a special boat to go off to wrecks. With financial and moral support affirmed, a group of prominent South Shields citizens soon followed up their idea promoting a design competition for, and the subsequent construction of, a boat intended to traverse inshore surf in safety. The resultant "life-boat" manned by brave and experienced men, soon proved its ability to save life and property in what had hitherto been regarded as impossible circumstances.

Throughout the next decade, the usage of such "life-boats" remained purely local, but in the following few years they were supplied to various other British ports, and some were even sent abroad. Additionally, in 1802, the successful prosecution of a petition of invention to Parliament by the boats' constructor, Henry Greathead, achieved widespread publicity for the "life-boat" and further stimulated demand.[4] Greathead's personal success and reward however did not go unremarked, provoking a controversy over who actually was the 'inventor' of the Shields "life-boats" which has continued to this day.

More generally, the first two decades of the nineteenth century saw the spread of lifesaving activities to many parts of Britain's coasts and, whilst such activities remained in the hands of locally-based organisations, the 'Shields' (or 'North Country') type of lifeboat continued to have many adherents. However, with the increasingly widespread establishment of lifesaving stations and, in 1824, the formation of a "National Institution for the Preservation of Life from Shipwreck", the defects and limitations as well as the virtues of the 'Shields-type' lifeboats gradually became more apparent. Tragically, the trigger to the type's final decline was the capsize of a South Shields lifeboat itself, the *Providence*, in 1849, with the loss of twenty crew.[5] This event presaged a national lifeboat design competition and the reformation of the earlier "Shipwreck" society into the now world-famous Royal National Lifeboat Institution.[6] The forward-looking steps of this new Institution soon sealed the national fate of the 'Shields-type' lifeboats. Ironically, but most appropriately, these forward-looking steps were taken under the auspices of Algernon, fourth Duke of Northumberland, son of the 'Shields-type's earliest patron.

Chapter One
Some Forerunners

Although the call for a lifesaving service at the mouth of the Tyne has often been represented as having occurred in isolation and as a purely local initiative, it may well have been that this was not altogether the case. It is difficult to prove or disprove the absorption of direct influences from elsewhere, but the very nature of the community in the then expanding seaport town of South Shields, and in particular its commercial and individual personal links with the London area, indicate the potential for the informal, or even formal, spread of information relating to new developments in maritime matters.[1] For instance, the gibe was made later by Lionel Lukin (1742-1834), a London-based claimant to the invention of the Lifeboat, that he had:[2]

> *"...no curiosity to enquire into the local squabbles of a remote country town..."*

But nonetheless, it was true that the most significant adoption of his own "Unimmergible Boat" patent (1785) had taken place not on the Thames, but on the Northumberland coast (less than forty miles from Shields), under the auspices of a noted local churchman, Archdeacon John Sharp (1723-1792).

Since the mid-1700s, Sharp had successfully introduced measures to assist coastal shipping and provide aid for distressed seafarers in the vicinity of his part-time residence, Bamburgh Castle in north Northumberland. This work was carried out both as a matter of personal initiative and, more formally, in his capacity as one of the five trustees (1755-1792) of the Bishop Crewe Charity, a well-endowed charitable organisation founded by Nathaniel Lord Crewe, Bishop of Durham, in 1719. Succeeding his father as a trustee in 1758, Dr. John Sharp eventually rose to the position of senior trustee, taking a leading role locally in the development of a dispensary, schools and services for mariners.[3] At the same time and at his own expense, he undertook the restoration of the castle to habitable condition, particularly after his appointment as curate for Bamburgh in 1773. In fact, works which were beneficial both for seaman and for the castle's fabric had commenced as early as the last year of his father's life, in 1757. Then the central tower had been restored so that it should not lose its purpose of having been "...a sea mark for ages", a function whose continuance Sharp later ensured by establishing a fund for its future maintenance.

In his own words, Sharp's concern for maritime safety had been aroused by:[4]

> *The number of wrecks on this particular coast of vessels that had run for Holy Island harbour in a storm and failed of getting into it, and the melancholy sights of persons wrecked on the (Farne) islands and starving with cold and hunger, together with the savage plundering of such goods etc., as were driven on shore...",* events which had induced *"...the Lords of the Manor to give every assistance to vessels in distress, and premiums for saving lives."*

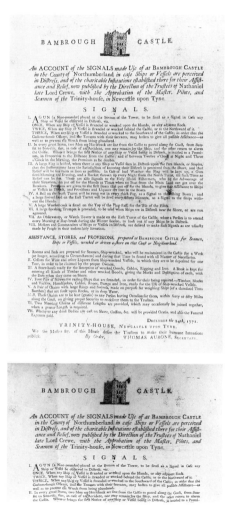

1. Part of archdeacon John Sharp's notice to mariners, c.1770, detailing his Bamburgh Castle-based services to shipping and seamen in distress.

2. Bamburgh c.1820. Despite this view's heightened drama and topography, Bamburgh's shoreline was (and still is) no place to be "with a storm coming on".

3. A coble off Bamburgh, c.1840. Sharp's coble, sent south to Lukin in 1789, must have looked much like this.

Sharp's interest had apparently been focussed by an unfortunate case in which a shipmaster who had come safely ashore subsequently "...died of a damp bed in the village...", leading him to set-up a dispensary that was followed in due course by other measures which, by the 1780s, included: a winter and bad weather coast watch with beach patrols; flag, gun and rocket signals to indicate ships seen in distress; warning signals by bell and gun during fog; facilities for receiving and accommodating shipwrecked mariners; storage for wreck materials; the provision of equipment such as "screws" (jacks) and chains for raising or weighing (lifting) stranded or sunken ships respectively; premiums (payments) to the first boats going off to distressed vessels; and, last and most final, a service whereby "Dead bodies cast on shore are decently buried gratis".

These measures were widely publicised through the issue of handbills and by notices inserted in local newspapers, as for example that in the *Newcastle Courant* of January 27th, 1776, indicating the publication of a print "...adorned with an elegant S.E. view of Bamburgh Castle ... also an East view of the Great Tower ... published by the Crewe Trustees with the approbation of Trinity House, Newcastle". The noted Newcastle engraver, Ralph Beilby, had been commissioned to produce the "elegant views" and Sharp's grasp of the realities of maritime practice is shown by his instructions that the resultant illustration should show the castle from the north or seawards (the viewpoint of shipping) for the purpose of easier recognition, especially by "foreign crews".[5] Although essentially and genuinely philanthropic, Sharp's measures also contained an element of self-interest in, for example, the protection from plunderers of 'wreck' (i.e. material from wrecks) which might prove useful to him for "...the purpose of building or (for any) manner it would answer best...". And, despite his recognition of such moral paradoxes as "How are warlike preparations consistent with charitable purposes?", he still recommended the establishment of a gun battery at Bamburgh for the defence of coastal shipping from enemy privateers in times of war.

Certainly Sharp's circle of contacts seems to have been quite wide, as shown by his correspondence with the Trinity Houses of both Newcastle and London, especially that berating the latter, in 1874, for the inadequacy of the warning 'lights' on the Farne Islands.[6] Indeed, it may well have been Sharp's influence which led to them granting a lease soon afterwards to Captain John Blackett for the erection of two lighthouses there in 1776, the first such 'lights' to effectively mark these major navigational hazards.[7] The same Captain Blackett, to whom the Crewe Trustees also gave permission to acquire land and erect a house at Bamburgh, certainly played a role in Sharp's next maritime safety venture – the provision of a special boat to go to the aid of ships in distress. This action followed a visit to Bamburgh in the summer of 1788 by Henry Oxenden Esq. of Broome, near Canterbury (Kent), whom it seems drew Sharp's attention to an "Unimmergible Boat" design which had been patented in 1785 by Lionel Lukin (1742-1834), a coachbuilder of Longacre, London. This design had previously been publicised via the Repertory of Arts (3rd volume) and through Lukin's personal contact with the Prince of Wales, the first Lord of the Admiralty, the deputy-master of Trinity House (London), and various aristocratic persons including Hugh, Earl Percy, the second Duke of Northumberland.[8] Upon returning to London in September 1788, Henry Oxenden wrote to Sharp that:[9]

> *"On my arrival in London, I immediately called on Mr. Lukin the Patentee for the boat which I had recommended to you, and not finding him at home I left a note desiring that he would send me a plan or model; and at the same time to let me know whether he would allow you to build on his plan if he was paid the common profit arising from such a boat – there is enclosed you his answer..."*

Although Lukin was anxious that Sharp should take up his design, which had:[10]

> *"...answered my intention in every experiment that has been made ..."* he raised an understandable reservation over seeing such boats being, *"...built in the Country (outside London) where I cannot inspect them, and that (objection) is, the reluctance of the builder in allowing any merit to an invention in which they have no share, and their proneness to throw Impediments in the way of its success..."*

Meanwhile, Henry Oxenden arranged for a friend, Mr. Holford of Lincoln's Inn, London, together with Captain Blackett who, fortuitously, was "...on the spot and a seaman", to inspect and assess Lukin's experimental boat. Blackett at least was not particularly impressed, although willing to go along with the idea provided it was a 'North Country' boat of the coble type which was subjected to the necessary modifications:[11]

> *"October 16th, 1788 Capt. J. Blackett (London) 'Sir, according to your desire I have made all the information I could in regard to the cork boat. Mr. Holford and self went to Mr. Lukin the patentee to know what he had to say in regard to the Construction of it, which (?) thought was very little to the purpose and of so simple construction that could be of very little or no use to Community the whole matter is no other than Cork sowd together like a Cork Jackett so run along the outside of the gunwail of the Boat and Extended about one foot under the gunwail and planck'd over with thin planck Which makes her Stiffer when she lays down to Leeward but they are constructed for Sailing boats in the river only. Their Keel is made of Iron Six Inches deep and weight Near Six hund. wgs. and Sharp as a Knife besides carries Eighteen*

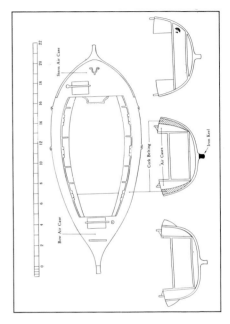

4. Lionel Lukin's patent allowed for a wide variety in type and disposition of flotation chambers to provide "unimmergible" qualities (after original Patent application, 1785).

hund.wgs. of Ballast they run against a lighter in Long reach and Stove a hole in her When she sunk to the Bottom and liked to have drown'd them. Mr. Wood and I went to see the vessel which is only a Common Peter Boat fortified as above .... I think the best way would be to have a good Coble Built and send her up here and lett them cork her according to the patent then She can both Row and Sail – Mr. Holford and I went to Lambeth to the Builder butt could not make him understand the nature of a Cobill - ".

Henry Oxenden had also firmly expressed the view to Sharp that a local, Bamburgh coble should be used:[12]

"...I thought it should be something of the coble kind to suit your flat shore, which is totally different from anything that is constructed in the river (i.e. on the Thames) ... a coble is the only proper boat for your purposes, your being already provided with one will enable you to make the trial at a very inconsiderable expense..."

Lukin's proposed fee for modifying boats to achieve his "unimmergible" principle was "...computed by multiplying the extreme length by the extreme breadth in feet and inches at six pence p. foot, so that for a boat 20 feet long and 7 feet wide I shall receive £3-10s-0d. (£3·50p.)", whilst new-built boats to his design were reckoned to cost around one-third more than those of conventional build.

By November of 1788 Sharp seemed, in Henry Oxenden's words "...to be determined to make the experiment...", but presumably with the approach of winter, when many coastal vessels ceased trading, he deferred sending his coble southwards until the following spring, and even then the uncertainties of transport by sea are indicated in the letters from his 'agent' at Bamburgh, George Hall:[13]

"March 28th, 1789. I have just received yours (i.e. Sharp's letter), will take care to send the coble by Wilson who is expected at Sunderland (i.e. North Sunderland, now commonly known as Seahouses, Northumberland) every day and will give directions with him..."
"April (?), 1789. "...this week I had the coble takin to Sunderland Harbour to go with Wilson's Friendship *but the weather appearing so strong he durst not take her this voige but hopes the weather will be more favourable when the packitt (i.e. scheduled trading vessel) comes and will take the boat with him..."*
April 11th, 1789. "...Capt. Wilson took the coble with (him) after all and I did not know it till today therefore have wrote Mr.

Lukins (sic) by this days post the ship sailed on Monday."

Frustratingly, there is no apparent record of the coble's actual return date, or authenticated instances of its subsequent use, though in his later memorial to the Prince of Wales (1806)[14] Lukin states that "Of the success of this boat, after it had received my alterations, I had very satisfactory accounts, having been informed that by the use of it many lives were saved in the course of the first year", a statement which is echoed in other, more local, printed sources. Surprisingly though, no mention of its use occurs in descriptions of wrecks in the surviving letters of George Hall to Sharp for 1790-91.[15] Similarly, it is not mentioned in Steele's nineteenth century "Sailing Directions", although detailed descriptions are still given there of the signals and shipwreck assistance provided from Bamburgh Castle's "most excellent institution".[16] So, whether this modified coble actually gained acceptance as a lifesaving boat is still unknown – the encumbrance of cork around the gunwale and weighted keel seem unlikely to have endeared it to fishermen whose prime requisites in a boat were light weight (for rowing and beaching) and handiness – and perhaps it did not long survive Archdeacon John Sharp's death in 1793.

There can, however, be little doubt that Sharp's activities had done much to justify his statement that "...now by means of lighthouses... and our own institutions for the safety of navigation our coast is safer than it ever was before and very few accidents happen". Throughout the age of sail, though, such "safety" – in an area renowned for its swift tides, low islets and isolated rocks, together with its exposure to easterly gales and frequent fogs – would always remain a somewhat relative matter.

Fortunately for posterity, Sharp's activities were well publicised and recorded but he was by no means the only individual in this late eighteenth century 'age of enlightenment' to recognise, and attempt to reduce, the suffering and death caused by maritime accidents and shipwreck. Of particular note (having followed a Dutch example) was the formation in 1774 of a "Humane Society for the Recovery of Persons Apparently Drowned" (later, the Royal Humane Society) in London. This, together with a similar organisation founded in Liverpool, quickly formed models for other such societies in many large coastal and seaport towns. The methods of resuscitation promoted by these societies, including mouth-to-mouth ventilation, proved remarkably effective in capable hands, with the Liverpool scheme achieving an astonishing 72% success rate over its first fifteen years of operation. It is not surprising to find that those concerned with this service in Liverpool considered not only the "recovery" of persons apparently drowned, but also measures for the prevention of drowning, particularly through the provision of a boat to attend wrecks around the busy and dangerous Formby Channel in the Mersey approaches.[17] The chief proponent of this scheme seems to have been Captain William Hutchinson, Dock Master and Water Bailiff for Liverpool from 1759-1793, a period which spanned one of the port's most dynamic and burgeoning eras. His remarkable career had commenced with an active life at sea in both the home and foreign-going trades, followed by a prominent position in Liverpool. He involved himself not only in the management of its new wet-dock system but also in progressive and humanitarian work in the fields of: tidal measurement; lighthouse improvement; regulated pilotage services; the 'Humane Society'; a marine dependents charity (1789); and, last but not least, the authorship of one of the eighteenth century's most important maritime works *A Treatise on Practical Seamanship* (1777). Co-incidentally, although not unusually for a seaman of this period, Hutchinson indicated that his formative experiences as a seaman were gathered in the North East coal trade, where he had "...been early in life at sea, in a small collier, where the first of my time, I was cook, cabin boy, and beer drawer for the men."

Perhaps it was also from this time that, although admittedly never shipwrecked himself, he conceived the strong feeling that:

> "... *To be in any way aiding and assisting to save the lives of people from ships that are forced, or lost, upon a lee shore, must be allowed to be one of the highest acts of humanity and charity that mankind is capable of performing, and deserves the highest praise and the most grateful acknowledgements that are possible to be given".*

Nonetheless, his seaman's pride and realism led him to stress that the actions taken by those on board a ship driven onto a lee shore were often the best, or only, remedy for achieving their safety, though he also recognised that "success in many situations may depend greatly on assistance from people on shore ..." It was exactly for providing such " assistance from people on shore ..." that he suggested, or at least supported, the establishment of a service which is succinctly noted on a contemporary chart as providing the following: "On the Strand (i.e. beach) about a mile below Formby Lower Land Mark there is a Boat House, and a Boat kept ready to save Lives from vessels forced on Shore on that Coast, and a Guinea, or more, Reward is paid by the Corporation for every human Life that is saved by Means of this Boat etc."

Unfortunately, the exact date of this service's establishment is not known, though it seems likely to have been in the early 1770s, but it is clearly recorded that by 1777 it had become a dedicated lifesaving service maintained by Liverpool Common Council with a salaried 'boatkeeper' and crews "... handsomely rewarded ... not less than one guinea per head for every Life or person they shall save ... to be paid out of the Dock Duties".[18] Regrettably, the surviving evidences give no positive clue as to the nature of the boat provided for this lifesaving station, though on practical grounds alone it would seem likely to have been of a type familiar to the shore-dwellers of the Formby area, perhaps a progenitor of the later, famous Mersey gigboats, or a large naval or merchant ship's boat of the period. Had it been a boat specially-built or modified in any way, it seems probable that Hutchinson would have alluded to

PROPOSALS

FOR THE

RECOVERY of PERSONS APPARENTLY DEAD.

I.

PLAN for the RECOVERY of PERSONS apparently dead by DROWNING.

1st. THE Governors of the Dispensary have engaged accommodations for the reception of drowned persons at the following public-houses, viz:—The *Coal Exchange Coffee-house*, on the Quay, at Newcastle; the sign of the *Shepherdess*, a little below the Custom-house Quay, at North-Shields; the sign of the *King of Prussia*, at the Ferry-boat landing, in South-Shields; at the sign of the *Ship-Launch*, Howdon Pans; and at the *Hotel* at Lemmington. And, when accidents happen at any distance from the above *Receiving-houses*, the Governors of the Dispensary engage to pay the expence which any publican or other person may sustain by receiving the unfortunate object into his house.

2d. The instruments and medicines, necessary for the recovery of persons apparently dead, inclosed in a proper box, shall be kept, in constant readiness, at the *Receiving-houses*, for the use of the Medical Assistants.

3d. Wooden pipes, which may be used by any of the by-standers, shall also be lodged at the *Receiving-houses*, and at one public-house in each village, on both sides of the river, from Newburn to Tynemouth; and the landlords shall have orders to give one to any person, who may apply for it, for the recovery of drowned objects, upon his leaving his name, and promising to return the pipe.

4th. The Medical Gentlemen at Newcastle, North and South-Shields, Howdon Pans, Swalwell, Winlaton, and Newburn, have generously offered their aid as Medical Assistants.

5th. A premium of one shilling shall be offered to the messenger who shall bring the first Medical Assistant to the patient: This reward is requested to be advanced by the Medical Assistant.

6th. The Medical Assistants shall be empowered to distribute a reward, not exceeding five shillings, to the persons they shall employ to assist in the methods of recovery, provided they persevere for four hours or upwards.

7th. If the drowned person be in ability, and recover, it is to be understood, that he shall defray the expence of his accommodations; or, if he cannot be restored, the same is expected from his relations.

RULES to be observed by the Spectators for the RECOVERY of PERSONS apparently dead by DROWNING, recommended by the MEDICAL SOCIETY of Newcastle.

Rule I. As soon as the body is taken out of the water, a person must inflate the lungs of the patient, by blowing into the mouth, or, (which is better) into one nostril, thro' a wooden pipe, a roll of cap-paper, or any thing else that will effectually convey the breath up the nostril; and whilst the other nostril, together with the mouth, is closely shut, that no air may pass otherwise than by the pipe. At the time of blowing thro' the pipe, another person, in order to prevent the air getting into the stomach, must gently press the projecting part of the windpipe backwards. When the lungs are filled, the person must remove his hand from the mouth and nose, and press the belly and breast, so as to let the air pass out. When by these means the lungs have emptied themselves, the blowing thro' the pipe is to be repeated in the same manner, so that natural breathing, as far as possible, may be imitated. If the lungs cannot be, by these means, distended, it most probably will proceed from some stoppage about the opening into the windpipe, which stoppage, if possible, should be removed, by pulling the tongue forwards, before air

ticularly mentioned in the end of Rule V. must be continued for a long time: Perseverance is absolutely necessary; and it is often only after two, three, or four hours of uninterrupted labour, that the first signs of life appear. But great moderation must be observed in the use of all the means, especially in the application of heat; for placing the body before a hot fire, and rubbing it too violently, are always prejudicial, and often destroy the feeble remains of life.

VII. If signs of life appear, which may be known by slight sighing or gasping, any liquid cordial, such as wine, brandy, or geneva, largely mixed with warm water, may be given by a tea-spoonful at a time; and if the powers of swallowing have returned, these cordials ought to be repeated, but still with moderation.

VIII. Altho' the above methods of cure ought to be immediately begun by any of the by-standers of discernment, and have been often attended with the happiest effect; yet, as the application of the means requires skill and dexterity, and as it is frequently absolutely necessary to employ instruments to inflate the lungs, one or two of the Medical Assistants should be called in without delay. The loss of every moment, or the misapplication of the means, is attended with the utmost hazard to the unfortunate object, who may be approaching nearer and nearer to a state from which he cannot recover.

** Persons apparently dead from HANGING, are to be treated in the same manner as those who are drowned. And persons seemingly dead by exposure to intense FROST, are to be treated as mentioned in Rule III.

II.

DIRECTIONS for recovering Persons suffocated by the noxious Vapours or DAMPS of COAL-PITS.

1st. The person suffocated must be removed, with the utmost speed, to the cool and open air. The lungs must be instantly inflated, in the same manner as directed for drowned persons (Rule I.); and cold water should be thrown, in small quantities, upon the face, and even over the whole body.

2d. These practices should be continued, without intermission, for some time; but, if they prove ineffectual, and the body become cold, it must be dried and carried home, in the same posture as directed for drowned persons (Rule IV.); and then warmth may be cautiously applied, by gently rubbing the surface with warm flannel, and by applying bottles of hot water, wrapt up in flannel, to the feet. But much heat will always prove destructive; for persons recovering by cold applications, have relapsed when taken into a heated room.

3d. Blowing air into the lungs should be still continued, the doors and windows kept open, and no more persons should be admitted into the room than are absolutely necessary for assistance.

4th. The methods of treatment should be continued for a long time; for instances have occurred, where persons have not recovered till after twelve hours persevering labour.

** Persons suffocated by the foul air of WELLS, VAULTS, and DITCHES; by the fumes arising from FERMENTING LIQUORS, burning CHARCOAL, and QUICK-LIME, are to be treated in the same manner.—But, in all these cases, a Surgeon should be sent for as soon as possible, as the lungs very frequently cannot be inflated without such instruments, as it would be improper to place in the hands of every spectator.

III.

PLAN for the RECOVERY of PERSONS apparently dead by DROWNING.

1st. THE Governors of the Dispensary have engaged accommodations for the reception of drowned persons at the following public-houses, viz:—The *Coal Exchange Coffee-house*, on the Quay, at Newcastle; the sign of the *Shepherdess*, a little below the Custom-house Quay, at North-Shields; the sign of the *King of Prussia*, at the Ferry-boat landing, in South-Shields; at the sign of the *Ship-Launch*, Howdon Pans; and at the *Hotel* at Lemmington. And, when accidents happen at any distance from the above *Receiving-houses*, the Governors of the Dispensary engage to pay the expence which any publican or other person may sustain by receiving the unfortunate object into his house.

5. Parts of a Tyneside "Humane Society" handbill, from the Lawe House Collection. Such activities were discussed locally by at least May 1789.

such practices in his Treatise, where the only modification described in his substantial section "On Preserving Boats from Foundering when Ships Founder", is that for rigging a temporary "sea anchor".

By the last quarter of the eighteenth century it does seem that, for the first time in Britain, some formal attention was being given to the philanthropic and practical aspects of saving life from shipwreck. The motives for such work were, like the individuals concerned, probably rather mixed, but as expressed by Hutchinson and Lukin respectively, there was recognition of both humanitarian ideals and the practical needs of a maritime Nation State:[20,21]

> *"...lives are undoubtedly of more importance than ships. These may be renewed, but they are of little purpose without good crews to navigate them; and the difficulty we now meet with, in manning both ships of war and merchant ships, should teach us to use every possible method to preserve the lives of our brave seamen..."*

> *"...to rescue from a watery grave many whom business or pleasure may have exposed to a tempestuous sea ... (and) to save annually a great number of lives highly useful to the state, and invaluable to their several families; would be (an idea to be) received with utmost avidity..."*

To save a life was of course also to save a putative soul, and the religious principles behind lifesaving are clearly indicated in the work of men such as Dr. John Sharp and William Hutchinson. Indeed, the latter's short anecdote of reviving one of his seaman who was "apparently drowned", well illustrates this aspect:[22]

> *"...the first words he was able to speak (perceiving me busy about him) were "My dear Captain pray for me". To which I replied, that as he was now in a fair way of recovery, I hoped he would be able to pray for himself, and be thankful to Providence for his narrow escape."*

Whether or not the work of men such as Sharp, Lukin and Hutchinson had any direct influence on the next major lifesaving development, at South Shields in 1789, must on known evidences remain 'unproven'. But, what does seem more certain is that the Shields development was very much in line with the mood of those late eighteenth century maritime times.

6. Dunstanburgh Castle, Storm Clearing Off, aquatint after T. M. Richardson, 1820. The depiction of wreck or wreckage in local artists` work is a contstant reminder of the toll exacted by the Northumberland coast.

Chapter Two
Shields: Wreck and Response

That the loss of the ship *Adventure* of Newcastle in 1789 preceded the activities which led to the development of a purpose-built, lifesaving boat at South Shields in that year has never been in doubt. This sequence of events is confirmed in contemporary accounts by one of the principal figures involved, Nicholas Fairles. It is also directly alluded to in material issued by the Lifeboat's builder, Henry Greathead, and the published evidence of a Parliamentary Committee of 1802. Curiously, this last publication included a factual error which was repeated up until recent times, post-dating the wreck of the *Adventure* by five months to September of 1789 instead of March of that year.[1] Co-incidentally, an error also seems to have occurred over the date of the introduction of Sharp's lifesaving coble which all secondary sources give as 1786, the year following Lukin's patent for an "Unimmergible Boat". This is definitely three years too early, the coble actually having been sent south for modification only in April 1789, a few weeks after the loss of the *Adventure*.

1. Wreck at Tynemouth, 1828, by T. M. Richardson. A graphic reminder that wrecks were as much about loss of property as loss of life.

Quite what it was about the wreck of the *Adventure* which turned local concern into concerted action still remains a little unclear. But the vessel's loss contained a number of elements which suggest that it may have transformed an almost commonplace accident into public tragedy: she was unlucky, since despite groundings and difficulties the rest of the fleet of returning, light (in ballast) colliers to which she belonged finally made port safely; her master's attempts to beat offshore and twice anchor were seamanlike expedients which would have gained the understanding and empathy of a seafaring population; the process of wreck, extending over a day and a half, terminated close inshore on a Sunday, giving opportunity for a maximum turnout of bystanders from the town, for the most prominent of whom it would also have been a churchgoing day; as a Newcastle-owned vessel,[2] and 'constant trader' to the Tyne, there would be immediate (and in some cases personal) identification with the crew's plight; and there was major, observable loss of life, but quite miraculously five of the ship's complement of thirteen were saved as the tide receded. The reaction of the two local newspapers also seems somewhat unusual, with coverage extending well beyond their usual plain and factual reports. That of the *Newcastle Advertiser* was notable not only for its length but also its dramatic content, suggesting perhaps some personal involvement by the reportee:[3]

2. Boxhauling – the kind of emergency manoeuvre which the *Adventure's* master may have tried in vain (from Hutchinson's *Treatise on Practical Seamanship*).

3. Part of the Newcastle Custom House Shipping Register entry for the ill-fated *Adventure*. Her shipboard register was "lost" in the wreck.

"On Saturday last (i.e. 14th March) a large fleet of light Colliers arrived at this port, the greatest part of which got into the harbour with difficulty. – Numbers of them struck in coming over the Hard Sand, being driven to leeward by the Northerly wind and strong flood tide, but providentially escaped being wrecked. The Adventure, *Strachan, master, was doomed to a less happy fate, and exhibited such a picture of distress as cannot be described. After endeavouring to reach the Bar, but in vain, and to clear the land with as little success, they were obliged to bring up at anchor in very shallow water, where they rode until Sunday morning, when they cut from their anchor, and made a second attempt to get off the shore, but all to no purpose, so that they were compelled to let go another anchor in a still worse situation than before. – Here they rode in a most tempestuous sea till past twelve o'clock; when the ship parted from her anchor, and came ashore. She kept beating towards the land as the tide flowed, the sea every moment making a free passage over her, and in this most dismal situation continued for near five hours, when her masts went away, and soon after that she broke up. – In the meantime, it would have melted an adamantine heart to have observed the poor sufferers fly from mast to mast, and from one part of the vessel to another in search of safety. The master and seven men perished – Five of them were miraculously saved on pieces of the wreck."*

Tragic though this event was, it also serves to point up the fact that wrecks were not automatically accompanied by loss of life, since of the other vessels which went ashore on the Herd Sand during the same gale, the *Pitt, Holderness, Fortitude* and *Myrmidon* (of South Shields), all appear to have successfully "got off". And, despite the fact that the timber-laden *Frederica Sophia* of Eastrice, Denmark, (which struck soon after the *Adventure* broke-up) was reckoned likely to become a total loss, all her crew were saved. Indeed, in his 'Treatise' Hutchinson had described those measures which could be taken by ships caught on such lee shores in order to ensure that *in extremis* they were run ashore under control and in such a way that "...not only all the lives, but the ship and cargo may often be saved..."

One of the South Shields notables present, Cuthbert Heron (owner of the *Myrmidon*), apparently offered a reward to any boatmen who would attempt a rescue of the *Adventure's* crew, but none would take it up.[4] Perhaps the judgement of these men is supported by a brief note in the *Newcastle Courant* which records that on the same Sunday, off a neighbouring port[5] "...the sea being very high, a foyboat belonging to Sunderland was overset, and four men thrown out of her to the mercy of the waves..."; though providentially all "...were taken up". This does however serve to emphasise the inadequacy even of boats which were designed to service shipping off these river entrances, and manned by tough experienced crews, to effect rescues in onshore gales. In offshore winds it was not uncommon for such boatmen to be unable to regain their home ports and themselves require assistance from passing vessels. On occasion, though, local boats and men did carry out successful rescues and such actions might be rewarded by means of public subscription. For instance in the preceding winter of 1788, during an easterly gale, a Whitby sloop was driven upon the rocks at the Tyne entrance where "...the people on board remained in a situation too dreadful to be described, until near dark, when four brave seamen rescued them from their distress..."; the financial recognition of the "...zeal and humanity (of those) who so nobly adventured their lives..." soon reached over twenty guineas.[6]

It seems to have been an extension of this kind of public subscriptive activity, which was usually led by shipowners, that provided the first crucial step towards establishing a purpose-built boat for lifesaving in South Shields. Unfortunately, no single objective account of the very earliest stages of the matter survive but, despite its particular viewpoint, a later (1802) summary of events by an anonymous, local, magazine-contributor (styled "A Son of Tyne") gives a broad idea of the sequence of events. Even then, some twelve years later, there was still a vivid memory of the wreck of the *Adventure* "...a scene of distress ... as will not soon be effaced from the memory of those who were reduced to the necessity of being mere spectators (and) who could assist them only by their wishes..." and a natural understanding of the immediate consequence that:[7]

> *"This melancholy event roused the feelings of a number of Gentlemen, owners of vessels, who occasionally attended for the purpose of reading the newspapers, and seeing their vessels come in and go out of harbour, at an place built upon the sea banks, called the Lawe-House. A subscription was immediately opened, and a committee appointed to consider of the best means to guard against such dreadful accidents in future."*

Although his original letter now appears lost, one of these "Gentlemen, owners of vessels", Michael Rockwood, must quickly have contacted Trinity House, Newcastle, with suggestions as to how to "...guard against such dreadful accidents in future", for he received a reply (dated 6th April, 1798) which fortunately still survives:[8]

> *"I received your favour of yesterday with a plan for a boat and beacons inland, and agreeable to request laid it before the Trinity Board. I am authorised to tell you they highly approve of the plan and will lend it every assistance. Have likewise had an interview with Mr. John Airey and Mr. A. Adams of the Committee of the Coal Trade, who give the proposers of the plan every credit for the*

laudable attention, and think the boat itself should be built out of the fund invested in their hands, or at least a very handsome sum should be contributed towards it, but as they are only Trustees, they must be applied to by the Trade to authorise them to grant it. I need not point out to you the mode of application!"
(signed) Edward Shadforth jnr.

As the agency responsible, under Royal Charter, for the erection and maintenance of navigational marks on the North East coast, the Trinity House, Newcastle, automatically took over the request for 'leading' beacons at South

4. The development of the South Shields Market Square area, in the late eighteenth and early nineteenth centuries, symbolised the town's growing civic independence.

Shields— a matter which took a decade to mature – but although commending the "plan for a boat", passed this suggestion on for consideration and potential support by the Committee of the Coal Trade. Judging by Shadforth's final remark, this latter rather shadowy but influential body was well known to Rockwood, with the inference that personal links would now carry his plan through the necessary formalities. The practicalities of forwarding the proposed plan, however, were left in the hands of that publicly well-known group of South Shields citizens, to whom Michael Rockwood belonged, The Gentlemen of the Lawe-House, a group whose membership probably included a local branch of the Committee of the Coal Trade.

By the late eighteenth century South Shields had become a burgeoning rivermouth town of some 11,000 people, its community largely dependent upon coastal and Baltic shipping activities and their dependent trades, especially ship-repairing and shipbuilding, together with coalmining and the growing manufactories of various kinds which were replacing the dying salt industry. Latterly, there had been a marked increase in shipowning in the town with South Shields-based vessels figuring largely on the Newcastle shipping registers. Its shipowners had pioneered the formation of Mutual Insurance Clubs for their vessels, whilst its numerous seamen (though often considered a recalcitrant body by the standards of the time) were also known as a highly skilled and cohesive group of men, being particularly sought after during times of naval impressment. Shields had benefited greatly from the slow decline of Newcastle's hegemony over the Tyne and its trade and, though this old centre of power and the resultant rivalries were by no means things of the past, the town of Shields had gained much in commercial and civic independence. Its internal governance was maintained by a *Select Vestry* (or, *Four and Twenty*), consisting of twenty-four prominent citizens who dealt with the administration of the Poor Law, policing, the collection of rates, statutory pricing and a wide variety of similar matters. On a more informal note a group of some forty men – amongst whom were the leading property-owners, businessmen, mariners and shipowners – assembled in February 1788 to set-up *The Lawe-House* subscription newsroom. This, in the style of the times, appears to have been a 'coffee-house' where they could mix business with pleasure and pursue that most important of activities in a maritime community, the gathering of information. It was this relatively new organisation which set-up a small committee to further the aims of providing a boat, and supporting services, for the rescue of distressed mariners at the entrance to the Tyne.

Although little is known of the men who formed this *Lawe House Committee* – Nicholas Fairles, Henry Heath, Michael Rockwood, William Masterman, Joseph Wm. Roxby and, perhaps, Cuthbert Marshall—there are indications that as a group they were linked and had influence in a variety of ways. Nicholas Fairles was undoubtedly the most prominent citizen of late eighteenth and early nineteenth century South Shields. Descending from a Mayor of Durham, the Fairles family had become major property owners in the town, and, important figures in the heyday of the (now declining) salt industry. Eventually for Nicholas himself there was to be accession to a second large family estate, the breaking of a profitable Newcastle monopoly (the landing of ship's-ballast) and appointment to that most powerful and public of local positions – Justice of the Peace. In this last role he applied himself robustly during times of civil difficulty, an obituarist describing the somewhat uncompromising attitude needed for:[9]

> *"...suppressing, in his magisterial capacity, the petty squabbles and turmoils which must be constantly arising in a population composed of seamen, pitmen, and labouring people, such as that of South Shields and its neighbourhood..."*

Additionally, he was "...a zealous promoter of every local improvement..." and, with hindsight, seems to have played a considerable part in creating the image of South Shields as an identifiable entity.

His 'shipowning' interests, though, were relatively small, certainly less than those of Rockwood, Marshall and Masterman, all of whom held shares in more than half a dozen vessels during the period around 1789.[10] All three described their professions at sometime as "Mariners", with Marshall and Masterman also appearing as "Master Mariners" (i.e. ship's Masters), a title which at that time usually implied a major shareholding in a vessel, with responsibility for its commercial as well as seafaring operations. This also allowed them to adopt the status of "shipowner" with rather more substance to the claim than was the case with some quite minor shareholders in ships. Rockwood and Masterman were especially closely connected, as joint shareholders in at least four ships, with the former having a son named Thomas 'Masterman' Rockwood. Heath, the son of a Mayor of Hartlepool, and Joseph W. Roxby appear to have been typical shipowner-gentlemen through minor shareholdings, though unsurprisingly in such a community both had family links with ship's-masters. Four of the six men: Heath; Rockwood; Marshall; and, Masterman; later became founder members of an important new mutual insurance 'club' for local shipping, the *Equitable Insurance Association*, 1797. Underpinning such business and family ties there were civic duties too. Although by 1789/90 only Fairles and Marshall were in place as members of the Select Vestry, the remaining four were all elected to fill vacancies which occurred within the next five years. All six were also to be found involved in the affairs of St. Hilda's Church and Marshall was a chapel-warden there.[11]

That this Lawe House committee possessed the potential in terms of practical expertise, civic authority and access to finance, which was needed for commissioning a boat for saving lives can hardly be doubted. What they did not have, though, was the design for such a boat, since "boats of common construction" had proved inadequate for the job. It seems likely then that they did begin much as their "Chairman" Nicholas Fairles later recounted by:[12]

5. Subscription list of the Lawe House newsroom, 1791, including the signatures of: Fairles (1), Heath (10), Roxby (11), Marshall (13) and Masterman (22) Rockwood (34) was 'secretary'.

6. A caricature of late eighteenth century shipowners like the "Gentlemen of the Lawe House"; not everyone saw them as honest, altruistic pillars of society.

> *"...obtaining (information and) models of boats most proper for saving persons from ships wrecked at the entrance of this harbour; in consequence of which an advertisement appeared in the Newcastle paper."*

In truth, this now celebrated advertisement was a very modest affair, occupying less than two column inches:

> *"A REWARD of TWO GUINEAS will be given to any person producing a PLAN (which shall be approved of by the Committee appointed for that Purpose, as the best) of a BOAT, capable of containing 24 Persons, and calculated to go through a very shoal, heavy, broken Sea: The Intention of it being to preserve the Lives of Seamen, from Ships coming ashore, in hard Gales of Wind. Plans will be received on any Day, at the Law-House, South-*

Shields; and the Committee will meet at THREE o'Clock on the 10th of June, 1789, to determine who shall be entitled to the Reward. The Committee will be obliged to any Gentleman favouring them with his Hints, or sending a Plan prior to that Day."

The "Reward" of two guineas was attractive, but not excessive, the equivalent it should be said of around a month's wages for a skilled tradesman, or a little more than the lump-sum paid to a seaman for a typical round trip, Newcastle-London, in the coal trade. The advertisement, which first appeared on the 2nd May 1789 in the *Newcastle Advertiser*, was subsequently repeated elsewhere, but it gave respondents little more than a month in which to reply or prepare "a Plan". Perhaps this was the reason why the Committee met not on the 10th of June as advertised, but delayed for some five weeks before finally convening on the 22nd July to consider who had produced the "best plan".[13] This, however, proved a somewhat disappointing occasion since although suggestions had been received by letter from various individuals, Fairles recollections indicate that only two models of note were presented, one by a Mr. Wouldhave and the other by a local boatbuilder, Mr. Greathead. The former model, which had been with the Committee for five weeks, was in Fairles words, "...not approved by the Committee: and on my suggestion Mr. Wouldhave was presented with one guinea, as compensation for his trouble ..."[14] whilst the latter was "...also considered an improper one for the purpose wanted...". The Chairman's gesture towards Wouldhave was understandable since Wouldhave's surviving model illustrates that he had thought through (in theory) an innovative design and represented it by a well-fashioned model. But, unfortunately, Fairles placatory gesture seems to have backfired, being rebuffed by Wouldhave at the time and, worse still, remembered with rancour in later days:[15]

> *"...they offered me a guinea, as they said, Because I was Second - Then said I, Gentlemen, Who is first? There was no reply. a pause – I took the guinea, and gave it to Mr. Teasdale saying, Set this to my account; for I do not mean to pocket this..."*

Indeed, who was first? In the absence of other eyewitness evidence it is necessary to consider, with due reservations, the very specific account of events later related by Nicholas Fairles himself. The competitive approach engendered through the advertisement had obviously failed to produce a single definitive and acceptable design, although it had produced "Much information (which) was received by letter". And it also seems to have re-inforced some existing views of the committee, as for example in regard to the use of cork, which:[16]

7. The Lawe House committee's advertisement as placed in the *Newcastle Advertiser* of 2nd May, 1789.

*"Before any model was exhibited ... was recommended by a Mr.
Hays, of Alemouth (i.e. Alnmouth) in a letter to the committee;
but prior to that, the idea of cork existed with them and was
strongly recommended by me"*

That the progression of designing the boat was now considered the
province of the committee alone is clearly shown by Fairles comment that
with respect to Greathead,[17] "... the committee considered they had it in their
power to compensate him by employing him to build such a boat as they
should hereafter determine upon." Discussions within the committee
immediately ensued, and they "... endeavoured to combine, with their own
knowledge on the subject, the various information they had received, and out
of the whole to produce a something which might answer the purpose."
Despite agreement on some general principles and forms there was no
immediate decision, the matter eventually being forwarded by Fairles and
Rockwood who, during a casual encounter, produced their own compromise
model which, as previously agreed, was then "...ordered to be built by Mr.
Greathead, under the direction of the committee." Crucially, however, at a very
late stage in the proceedings Greathead suggested a modification to their
design – that the profile of the keel should be curved and not straight – a'
seemingly minor adjustment which was later to cause a major controversy.

Although it may be considered unwise to rely on a single personal source,
the account given by Fairles is so consistent with the behaviour of committees
past and present (information gathering, discussion and equivocation, decision
through default by chairman and secretary) that, even with additional wary
allowance for its retrospective viewpoint (1806), it still possesses a very
definite ring of truth. There was one further point upon which Fairles was
unequivocal:[18]

*"...I do declare, that neither Mr. Greathead nor Mr. Wouldhave was
the inventor of the Lifeboat".*

He felt it necessary to emphasise this statement since, by then, the former had
publicly substantiated the title of "inventor" with which to enhance his
somewhat unusual career.

Chapter Three

Henry Greathead: The Lifeboat's Builder

At the time of the Gentlemen of the Lawe House's advertisement, Henry Greathead had been established in South Shields as a boatbuilder for only five years, since 1785. His connection with the town however extended back to his early childhood when, in 1763, his father, John Greathead, who was Supervisor of Salt Duties at Richmond (Yorkshire), was transferred to South Shields to act in a similar capacity for the flourishing salt-producing industry there. Reputedly the youngest of twins, born in 1757, Henry was part of a family of thirteen and went, he said "...from inclination rather early to business, from which cause I preferred that of a boat-builder to a ship-builder merely from the lightness of the work after the expiration of my apprenticeship, in the course of which I had been made foreman.".

Fortunately, it is possible to gain an overview of his life, since during the latter part of his career, when he had acquired fame as "the inventor of the lifeboat", he was featured in a compendium of short biographies, *Public Characters of 1806.*[1] This, in addition to some predictable encomiums, printed a substantial portion of "...a manuscript account of his life". These autobiographical notes of Greathead's dealt with his adventures up until the commencement of his boatbuilding business and marriage in 1785-86. But, in view of the substantial publication which he himself had commissioned in 1804 to confirm his acknowledged recognition as "the inventor of the lifeboat", the manuscript did not deal with the events surrounding the already controversial origin and development of the lifeboat itself. His biographer contented himself on this score with elaborations derived from the "authentic information" which Greathead's publication of 1804 had contained.

Surprisingly perhaps the autobiographic manuscript is, if anything, an unadorned and understated account of Greathead's earlier life at sea between 1777 and 1783 in the merchant and naval services. The experiences which he recounts were certainly not atypical of those of a Shields seaman of this period, as is shown by comparison with the lengthier and fuller account given by his Shields-born contemporary, William Richardson (1768-1858).[2] But the particular experiences which Greathead underwent, the contacts which he inadvertently made, and the ideas and maritime practices to which he was exposed can, on circumstantial grounds at least, be seen to have considerable bearing on his later role in the origination and development of the lifeboat.

His biographer indicates that, at an early stage in life, Greathead was made aware of the fact that for advancement in the shipping trade or in setting up a business one needed "interest" (i.e. personal influence), or "capital" – of which his family had neither in sufficient measure. This being so, he soon took the same shipboard chances as many others by going to sea as a ship's carpenter, a position which his shipwright's apprenticeship had qualified him for and which, in theory at least, protected him (unlike the common seaman) from naval impressment. His first voyage was, quite typically, from Shields to Dantzig and the Baltic in the 'Baltic Trade', but feeling that this gave "...little prospect of wealth or advancement..." and that in such a trade "...his faculties could reap but little instruction or advantage...", he sailed (in March, 1778) aboard a vessel bound from Shields to Portsmouth to join convoy for Grenada (West Indies). His decision may have had another unspoken purpose. Impressment in Shields had become commonplace once more with the quickening of The American War of Independence (1775-1783), and all "who used the sea" were at risk, though less likely to be so on an outward-going, convoy-bound ship. In fact, within a few days of his leaving it was reported that "...a warm press had broken out at Shields ... when a great many useful hands were taken...", and over a hundred men were subsequently sent to join the fleet at the Nore.[5]

Greathead's voyage, though, was to be a short one for his vessel ran ashore at night, proving by daylight to be no more than a couple of miles from Calais. His own actions, he says, kept the crew from the dangerous expedient of leaving the ship in the damaged longboat, whilst his judgement that the ship would not break up before the tide fell (and the breakers receded) also proved correct. Having attracted attention, they were boarded by French soldiers who took possession of the vessel and conducted the crew ashore as prisoners. Although there was, as yet, no formal declaration of war between Britain and France, the latter had signed a *Treaty of Friendship and Commerce* with America (4th February, 1778) which included powers to detain British vessels; half-a-dozen Sunderland colliers were already thus impounded in nearby Dunkirk. Even the inexperienced Greathead was aware that the vessel had been lost in curious circumstances, the pilot's instructions to tack (turn down-Channel) earlier in the night had not been followed, and the vessel had been run onto a relatively safe weather shore, not a dangerous lee one. Since commercial considerations still overrode political ones, a French "court of admiralty" was convened at which Greathead said the ship's master "...affirmed that (the ship) was driven on shore by *stress of weather*." Greathead said that this "...was with a view of recovering the amount of policy of insurance." To this he could not agree "...neither in justice to my own conscience, nor the interests of the unknown insurers..." This decision, through whatever reason—honesty, naivety or self interest – served him well in later years. It was also immediately helpful in obtaining the sympathy of his French captors who, perhaps also through the influence of the Duchess of Kingston (then in Calais), soon allowed him to leave in the Scottish brig *Aldie* which had been similarly stranded, but which had proved unprofitable for the French to retain as a prize (captured vessel).

By coincidence the *Aldie* had also been bound for Grenada, and on calling at Spithead, where the crew were initially threatened with impressment, she was immediately sent in pursuit of the recently departed West India convoy; but this they failed to overtake, making the entire voyage unaccompanied. The later loss of his journal and the passage of time probably account for chronological errors here in Greathead's narrative, which ascribes these happenings to 1779, when they quite definitely occurred a year earlier in 1778. This is confirmed both indirectly through his mention of seeing a total eclipse of the sun during the trip to the West Indies, (which almost certainly was that of June 24th, 1778, and was observed, nearer 'home' "...at Alnwick by Mr. Hastings with a large reflecting telescope..."), and, more directly through surviving naval records. His entry into the Navy, though, did not occur for another few months, during which time the *Aldie* had reached Grenada, where Greathead left her to be "...engaged as mate of the *Carolina* ... then loading for Quebec and Montreal." In this vessel he narrowly avoided shipwreck again, when she was nearly swept ashore (by currents) during a calm, only to suffer somewhat differently a fortnight later when the *Carolina* was "...taken by the *General Putnam*, an American privateer (commerce raider) mounting twenty guns ...". Ironically, he was to spend much of the next five years in the British Navy attempting to prevent merchant transport ships, like the *Aldie* and *Carolina*, from suffering the same fate. The *General Putnam* soon carried the *Carolina's* crew into that great centre of privateering, New London (Connecticut), a place which throughout the American War of Independence acted as "a thorn in our sides" to the British.

At this stage in the war, prisoner exchanges were of fairly frequent occurrence, and Greathead wrote that after his arrival in New London he was:

> *"... sent in a short time after to New York in a cartel. On our arrival in that port I was impressed on board his majesty's sloop of War the* Scorpion*, where I remained above a year, and was then transferred to the* Vulture *another sloop of war."*

In reality the naval records relating to the *Scorpion* suggest that he did not reach New York town, for on the 22nd September 1778, the *Scorpion*, which as a guardship was lying off New City Island in the port's northern approaches, dealt with two incoming vessels carrying British prisoners:[4]

> *"P.M. anchor'd here a flag of truce with British Prisoners shifted the prisoners on board a forage vessel and sent them to New York dismiss'd the Rebel Flag. A.M. Anchor'd here an Inglish (sic) flag of Truce received on Board British Prisoners from her and sent her to New York ..."*

He probably arrived with this latter "flag of truce", from which men were actually "received on Board", since he is listed in the ship's muster book as having entered as from the 21st September 1778. Despite his own biographical statement that he was "impressed on board", impressment was not indicated (as was usual) in the ship's muster book itself,[5] so perhaps he simply accepted the inevitable by 'volunteering', an act which could have brought with it the payment of a small bounty. An immediate expenditure of 18s 7d. (93p) and other payments thereafter for "slop cloaths" (clothing bought from the ship's stores) most certainly bear out his remark that when taken by the privateer he

1. A late eighteenth century "Sloop of War" and one of its boats. Such small, overcrowded sloops were Henry Greathead's 'home' for five years.

had, "... lost all my effects"; but it was to be a few months before his outgoings could also allow for the purchase of tobacco.

Altogether, nine "British Prisoners from New London" were recorded as being aboard the *Scorpion* at this time, but the others were soon parcelled-out amongst other naval ships, leaving Henry Greathead as the only one of the group to be added to the *Scorpion's* own complement. Though entered as an able seaman it could be that his woodworking skills proved a factor in his, rather than any of his companions', retention on board. *Scorpion*, a brig-rigged (two-masted) 'sloop', mounting fourteen carriage guns on a single 95-foot, gun-deck, was little bigger than the largest 'colliers' with which Greathead would have been familiar, though certainly much more crowded, her regular complement of around 110 men being nearly ten times that of an average collier vessel. Originally bought by the Navy in 1771, the *Scorpion* had been sent out to America soon after the the outbreak of war (1775), where she was one of those "... small vessels (which) had been on the North American station for years, exposed constantly to the ravages of sea, ice and radically changing weather",[6] conditions which kept such ships undergoing constant shipboard repairs. As guardship her ship's boats and tender were also in frequent use: intercepting incoming vessels, chasing rebel colonists' craft in the vicinity (usually unsuccessfully) or even making short, coastwise trips. Her large cutter, a roomy type of ship's boat which was recognised for its seaworthiness and usefulness "...(in) boarding ships in bad weather and shifting Prisoners", appears to have been especially hardworked. Its needs feature frequently in the ship's log, for example, "... 2nd, 3rd, 4th October Carpenters employed repairing the large Cutter...", so it seems likely that Greathead's boatbuilding skills may well have been applied here.[7] These lightly-built boats were notoriously prone to damage and their clinker planking was difficult to repair.

Otherwise, with a near stalemate in the land war and the French fleet having recently been forced away to the south, life on the *Scorpion* off British-occupied New York must have been one of routine and tedium, marked only by the increasing severity of the winter with its "...fresh gales, fogs and hard frost...", or events such as occasional desertions, a flogging and the loss of a man from exposure (after having fallen overboard). Springtime brought a new Commander to the ship, Captain Samuel Osborn Esq., who seemingly imposed a more severe regime, with floggings rising to one or two a month. Henry Greathead was amongst the first to feel, quite literally, the new Captain's lash, for on Thursday, 10th June, Osborn logged that he had:[8]

> *"Punish'd Richard Noyes, John Laws, and Henry Greathead seamen with 2 Dozen Lashes each, for Drunkeness and Mutinous behaviour...".*

Drunkenness, through ample supplies of grog, leading to disobedience or neglect of duty was not uncommon, but the charge of "mutinous behaviour"

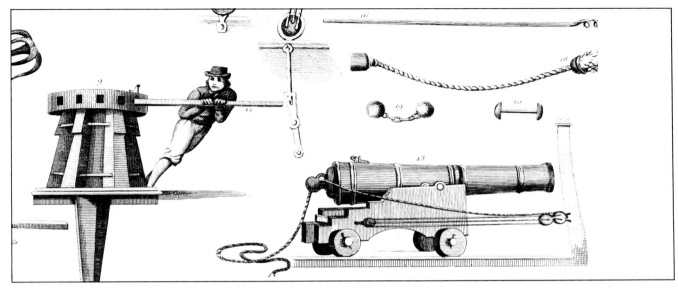

implies that this was a more serious breach of regulations, with an element of combination amongst the three men. Within a fortnight, however, there was much more to occupy the *Scorpion*'s commander and men, since she accompanied Sir George Collier's amphibious force northward to repel an unexpected rebel attack in Maine. Here her guns covered the attack on Newhaven and she took part in the landing and re-embarkation of the troops who burnt the townships of Norwalk and Fairfield. Returning to the anchorage off New City Island, *Scorpion* resumed guardship duties and it was here, in late November 1779, that Henry Greathead left her, transferring to a similar vessel, the ship-rigged (three-masted), sloop *Vulture*.

 Scorpion and *Vulture* had then been in company off and on for a fortnight, with Greathead being "lent to the *Vulture*" on the 12th November, though his appointment to her as carpenter's mate was not confirmed until the 28th, shortly before she proceeded to sea.[9] The transfer, which was also a promotion, may initially have come as something of a relief, for the *Scorpion* was in parlous condition, leaking so badly through rotten planking that she was reported as staying afloat only through the constant use of her handpumps, which were discharging no less than thirteen feet of water per day from her hold[10] (the ship's boats were also so worn-out that "... the small Cutter in launching broke in pieces being very rotten ..."). By comparison, *Vulture* was only three years old and fully seaworthy but very short of men, having recently lost six by desertion in New York, mustering some thirty below her official complement. The crew was a characteristic mix of the period, comprising

2. Life in the Navy in Greathead's day entailed much physical toil and hardship. All shipboard activity was dedicated to one ultimate aim – to service the great guns.

English and Irish seamen, pressed men from New York together with loyalist American volunteers; inevitably there was at least one other Tynesider! The conditions they were all about to endure were, by modern standards, appalling, but went unremarked by Greathead and his contemporaries, though even to them what followed must have appeared as something tougher than usual – winter patrol in the North Atlantic. The factual understatements of the ship's log (January 1780) are all that now remain to give a bare insight into what was encountered over the next seven weeks:[11]

> *"First part (early morning) fresh breezes with snow; Middle Latter (mid-late morning) Hard Gales and thick weather ... at 6 (evening) Close reef'd the Main Topsail and handed the Mizen Topsail – at 9 handed (took in) the Foretopsail ... haul'd up the Mainsail Endeavoured to Wear (turn the ship), but could not raise the Fore Tack, the block being Chok'd with Ice; by the severity of the weather four of the Men were frost-bit."*

> *"Middle, Hard Gales with Snow and Frost, Latter, Very Strong Gales ... a very heavy Sea running Ship'd a great quantity of Water."*

Despite a massive trans-Atlantic operation, the mis-direction and loss of transport ships had been so great that the British Forces in North America were also now facing one of the worst supply crises of the war. Whereas in the previous autumn aboard the *Scorpion* there had been the delight of fresh beef, here in mid-winter 1779/80 on the *Vulture* the victuals were so poor that the captain "...Survey'd Condem'd and Threw overboard 133 pieces of Beef of 9lbs. each that were Stinking Rotten and unfit for Men to Eat or be Kept in the Ship."

Worse was to come. On the 25th January whilst negotiating New York Harbour's notoriously difficult entrance the *Vulture* was caught by such a press of ice-floes coming down-channel that, despite all sail being set, she was forced back onto the shoals of the East Bank. Distress guns were fired, but the weather was so foul that she remained unheard and unseen, continuing to lay fast and at risk for a full week, until by a combination of good seamanship and ameliorated conditions she got-off and proceeded to New York for re-fitting. For the third time in less than a year Henry Greathead had faced the imminent danger of shipwreck. Back at sea in April they narrowly escaped wreck again when, having chased and driven ashore the privateer brig *Rattlesnake*, the *Vulture* only just managed to work herself offshore in the face of "...a very heavy swell ..." by slipping her anchors, an expedient only undertaken if the ship was at risk. But the *Rattlesnake* action, together with the taking of a tobacco-laden sloop soon afterwards, probably helped cheer the ship's company, though the resultant prize-money was probably small.

From June onwards the ship returned to guard duty in the Hudson River

3. The occupation of Rhode Island, 1776, by R. Cleveley. Henry Greathead was involved in similar, though smaller, amphibious operations in Maine in 1779.

north of New York, but even this period was not incident-free, for after various routine skirmishes with rebel raiders the *Vulture* sailed upriver (to the very 'front-line') on a clandestine errand. The most important rebel general in the northern area, Benedict Arnold, had made secret approaches suggesting he hand over his command to the British. So, the British General's adjutant, Major André, had been despatched in the *Vulture* to finalise arrangements with Arnold. But the plan went tragically wrong. At five-o'clock on the morning of the 22nd September, whilst André was still ashore meeting Arnold, the *Vulture* came under fire from a mysteriously and newly-positioned gun (or guns) on nearby Teller's Point. Quickly, whilst returning fire, *Vulture* was towed downstream against the tide and, within ninety minutes, had silenced the rebel battery – though not before having received:[12]

> *"... six shot in the hull and three through the boats on the chocks (with) standing and running rigging shot away in many different places ... The captain (only) slightly wounded ..."*

Ironically, Arnold managed to flee and join the *Vulture* but "the unfortunate Major André..." was captured and hanged as a spy. Not only did this aborted tryst result in repair-work for the *Vulture's* carpenters, but the discovery of Arnold's defection ruined the British plan to capture the strategic fort of West Point, a failure whose consequences may have prolonged the war for another two to three years.[13]

These three years were to see Henry Greathead, as he later commented:[14]

> *"... cruise all the way from Spanish River (north Nova Scotia) to St. Augustine, in the Floridas. I was (also) on board at the time she was commanded by Rupert George, Esq. on which occasion she engaged* Le Hermoine, *Captain La Touche, a French frigate of thirty-six guns."*

This last-mentioned action was one of the noted small ship engagements of the war, taking place on July 22nd of the following year, 1781. Having been sent north to Halifax (Nova Scotia), the *Vulture*, along with another sloop, two armed-ships and the 28-gun *Charleston*, was escorting a group of merchant ships. They were spotted off Cape Breton island by two 32-gun French frigates which, after a lengthy chase, brought the British ships to action as they successfully screened the merchantmen from attack. One of the weakly built armed-ships was soon forced to strike (surrender) and the *Charleston* (with badly-damaged rigging) slipped away after dark, as too did the other British warships.[15] But before this happened the *Vulture* bravely came to the relief of the hard-pressed *Charleston* by engaging the frigate *Hermione*, an adversary of more than twice her fire-power, for ninety minutes at "... a pistol shot's distance ...". Though suffering only two men killed and seven wounded, the *Vulture* suffered heavily in her rigging and upperworks, as was typical in an action with the French:[16]

> *"... our sails very much shattered, almost all the running rigging cut and great part of the Standing rigging, particularly of the Main Top-Mast having neither Stay, Shroud and Backstay but one to support it, two of our guns dismounted – Masts and Yards not materially wounded except the Main Mast and Main Yard..."*

On deck the harness casks (barrels) containing their supplies of pork and beef were smashed into unusable condition whilst, whether through despair or deception (it is now impossible to tell), the log records that at:

> *"... 3/4 past 9 opened the After Hold to get up the Rum for the Ship's Company and two puncheons ... 250 gallons ... was stove by shot and the whole of the Rum entirely lost..."*

After repairs the *Vulture* carried out further escort duties down the Canadian-American east coast out of Halifax, St. Johns and Penobscot before returning to New York's East River for a short while. From there she was sent south with convoys to the now beleaguered enclaves of Savannah and Charlestown (South Carolina) in the southern states, where the final collapse of the British effort to retain the American Colonies was shortly (1783) to take place. Although at last this long war was now dragging slowly to a close, with the major naval activities shifting to the West Indies and Gibraltar, ships such as the *Vulture* continued their duties much as before.

Patrols off the coast south of New York were followed, during 1783, by a trip southward to St. Mary's (north Florida) and Port Royal (near Savannah, South Carolina), before the commencement of a penultimate, 1,400 mile trip north again via New York to Halifax (Nova Scotia). From Halifax a final, four-week long, trans-Atlantic passage home saw her moored at Spithead by the 30th October. Though not long, this final trip certainly was crowded since, although 20 under her official crew complement of 125, she carried back a total of 50 extra persons in the form of marines, 'supernumaries' and loyalist American volunteers. As was always the case at the end of a war the ship's crew were soon paid-off, clearing the ship in early November, though the ship's carpenters seem to have been detained somewhat longer to help 'lay-up' the vessel.

Whether his time in the Navy had enabled Greathead to put together that "capital" which he evidently knew was necessary for success in business there must be cause to doubt. Promotion to ship's carpenter from carpenter's mate had been denied him, since this was one of the few positions which tied a particular man to a particular ship and William Murrant had been *Vulture*'s carpenter continuously since 1776. Neither, it appears, had the *Vulture* been

38

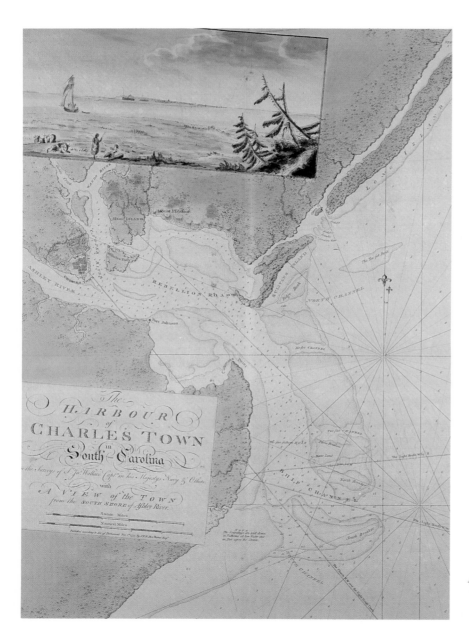

4. Chart of Charleston Harbour, South Carolina (from *The Atlantic Neptune*, 1776). *Vulture* grounded on this harbour's shallow bar in 1782.

successful in capturing valuable 'prizes', so with little more than a carpenter's mate's accumulated pay of around £1.10s (£1.50p) per month – against which were set his typical debts to the Navy of some £13 for "slop cloaths, tobacco and venereals" (this last two standard surgeon's 'fines' of 15s. each) – his finances would seem to have been strictly limited. But in terms of experience, if not wealth, there is little doubt that Greathead's naval service on the coast of North America had enriched his life in ways denied to many of his stay-at-home, or even merchant-seagoing, Shields contemporaries. There is good cause indeed to believe that those experiences contributed much to the expertise and attitudes which later moulded his claims to be "the inventor of the lifeboat".

5. These maps indicate the principal ports of call, and sea areas traversed, during Henry Greathead's eventful life at sea, 1777-1783.

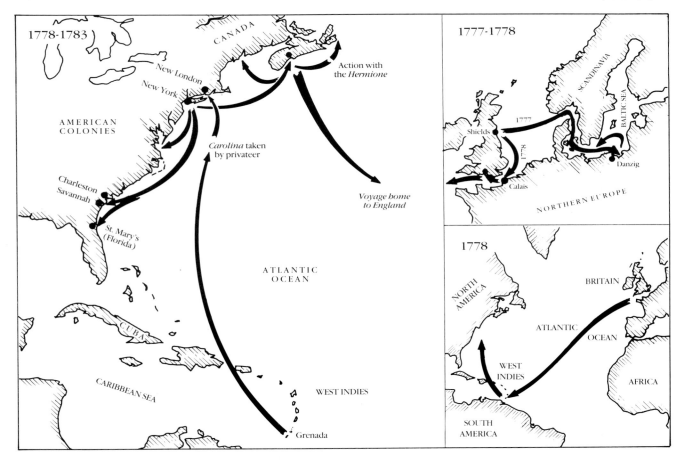

Chapter Four
The Origins of the *Original*

There is no clear evidence as to the exact date of build of the first lifeboat but since the "house" to protect it (together with distressed mariners and wreck goods) was underway by September 14th 1789, it seems likely to have been during this autumn period. Similarly, there is no specific date for the first use of the term "Life-Boat" to describe it, though it was current locally and then nationally by 1798 and 1802 respectively. The name *Original* for this first boat was quite definitely retrospective, possibly having originated either following the building of the second lifeboat in 1798 (which did bear a formal name, *Northumberland*) or sometime after Greathead's successful public campaign of 1802 to be recognised as the lifeboat's "inventor". Neither Fairles, Greathead himself nor Wouldhave's vociferous supporter, W. A. Hails, seem ever to have used the name *Original* when referring to this first boat.

Although certainly original in concept and dedicated function there is perhaps more question over how original the boat was with regard to its form and construction which, to a certain extent, some previous commentators have too readily considered as revolutionary and unique. Had the Lawe House committee followed the suggestions put forward by Wouldhave in designing the new boat, then this certainly would have been the case since his model embodied the new principle of self-righting and the technological leap forward to metal (copper) construction. With hindsight it can be seen that both innovations were simply too radical to be given serious consideration at the

1. Wouldhave's actual model of 1789. Of light tinplate construction with cork infill (57 cm length by 23 cm breadth), its weight of 3.2 Kg. indicates heavy ballasting. A contemporary account describes it as self-righting in seashore waves, but replica tests suggest it would not self-right from an inverted position in still water.

2. "Willie Wouldhave inventing the Lifeboat", by R. Hedley (1848-1913). This famous painting's clever composition and subdued narrative detail tells us much about a Victorian concept of the artisan-inventor, but little about this particular invention's complex history.

time; it was in fact over sixty years before self-righting was introduced to such boats and then against quite justified opposition by some. The cost of all-copper construction, even had it been a technical success, would plainly have been prohibitive; several decades were to elapse before successful seagoing boats were built in metal. If perhaps overly emphatic, Nicholas Fairles comment about Wouldhave's model[1] – that he did not derive "... any assistance from it in making up my ideas on the subject (i.e. of a lifesaving boat)" – can probably be taken in good faith, since even if the self-righting capability was appreciated it would have been considered of little consequence. Long experience proved that a boat's most important quality in coastal surf was that it should not "overset" (capsize) in the first place; even if righted an "overset" boat offered little hope of control or survival to its crew.

Taken simply as a literal pattern from which to build, Wouldhave's model also had serious deficiences:[2]

> *"...in form (it) much resembled a coal keel; the ends were alike – had what professional men call little rake, – and fully below. These two points required particular attention, as, in my opinion, the whole depended upon it..."*

These two points – the lack of rake (overhang) of the stems and the very rounded underwater shape at the boat's ends – were, from the contemporary local viewpoint, unacceptable features. Stem rake was needed to provide the boat with the reserve buoyancy necessary to lift over steep oncoming waves, whilst a sharp, unrounded entry was believed to allow a boat to "divide" the waves and thus make it easier to row. Such characteristics were readily demonstrable in that characteristic, vernacular boat-type of the region, the coble.

Regrettably, the only direct descriptions of Greathead's model were produced many years later, with those of Wouldhave and his protagonist, the South Shields-born shipwright, teacher and pamphleteer W. A. Hails,[3] being more derogatory than descriptive:[4],[5]

> *"Dare he (Greathead) say that his model in any way approached the form of a Norway Yawl? ... if it imitated anything, (it) was a butcher's tray, rounded at each end, in the form of a tailor's lap-board."*

> *"... (the) model was flat-bottomed, had nearly parallel sides, without any cork attached to them; semi-circular ends and very little sheer ..."*

Nicholas Fairles own brief and dismissive description adds little to explain the model's form, but a comment it contains does act as a pointer to the model's derivation:[6]

*"It was a long flat boat, and I think was to row double; that is
two persons on each thwart; nor were the ends alike. He
(Greathead) described it as being similar to a boat which he had
been accustomed to go up the rivers of America, in the night time,
under the command of some naval officer. This model had no
buoyancy by cork, nor did it resemble the lifeboat."*

Significantly, since it had been modelled on "... a boat ... under the command of
some naval officer...", there was no reference by Fairles to its resemblance to
common naval boats such as cutters, gigs, longboats and launches, with which
he and his companions, in seaport Shields, would surely have been familiar. All
three men, however, remembered its unusual flat-bottomed nature, a
characteristic of the specialised 'flat-boats' which were shipped-out from
Britain's south coast ports in great numbers for use during the amphibious
operations and troop-landings of the American War of Independence.
Greathead would certainly have seen such boats in operation on Collier's
expedition (1779) and during his time on the Hudson River. Though the
committee's rejection of such a boat for service in Shields' own ferocious
coastal surf was probably correct, Greathead had quite literally matched his
model to the advertisement's requirements. These troop-landing boats were of
shallow-draught design in order to make beach-landings through inshore
waters with, characteristically, a complement of up to 24 oarsmen who, as
Fairles described, rowed double (two to a thwart).

Having rejected these models, the Committee returned to better-known
ground by determining that the new boat's bottom should be "... something in
form between a coble and a yawl (i.e. 'Norway Yawl') ...". According to Fairles,
they then developed a clearer set of parameters within which to progress their
design:

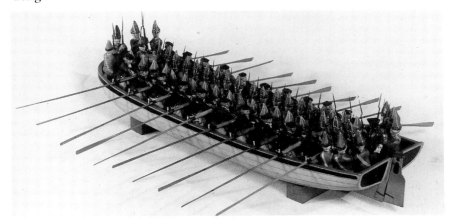

3. Model of a flat-floored, British troop landing
   boat. Greathead may also have seen some
   indigenous flat-bottomed boat types in the
   Baltic, and bateaux and dories in north east
   America.

"... buoyancy, and the ability to divide the water with the least possible resistance:— each end of the boat to be similar; that in leaving a wreck, there might be no occasion to turn the boat about; and thereby the danger of being laid athwart, or in the hollow of a sea would be avoided:— that great elevation at the ends was necessary, to prevent agitated broken water from entering the boat when contending against a head sea and wind:- and, finally the local situation required an easy draught of water ...".

Simply then the boat must be buoyant, easy to row, double-ended (pointed at both bow and stern), high at the ends and of shallow-draught. Whilst allowing perhaps for some retrospective analysis of the successful boat by Fairles, these requirements certainly fit a likely pattern of practical thoughts by practically-minded seagoing men. Rockwood particularly appears to have influenced the committee's early thinking, having "... described to them a boat by which he was saved at Memel (now, Klaipeda, Lithuania) ... in a most tremendous sea; she resembled the Norway Yawl...". Though a 'Norway Yawl's' deepish draught ruled out that hull-form for use at Shields, this line of thought would certainly have re-inforced ideas for a double-ended boat with low waist (centre) and high-sheered bow and stern.

Since there is no evidence to the contrary, it may be assumed that the clay model produced by Fairles and Rockwood accorded broadly with the above points.[8] In this medium (clay) it must have left much in terms of actual construction and detail for discussion with, or decision by, the builder. Of these individual decisions, the one which became most celebrated was the suggestion by Henry Greathead that the line of the keel should not be straight in profile but should be rockered[9] (deepest at the mid-point and swept up towards each end to merge into the raking stems). The thinking behind this modification was probably twofold, providing perceived advantages both in construction and usage. Since the boat was to be built with a bottom "... something in form between the coble and a yawl ..." it made sense to build it not with a conventional boat's keel, a vertical plank-on-edge structure, but with the well-known local cobles' 'ram plank', a plank-on-the-flat structure instead. In practice this could not be copied direct, since a coble's 'ram plank' had a double curvature, down towards its deep forefoot and up towards its shallow, square stern.[10] Constructionally, the needs of a double-ended boat would be somewhat different, but the principle of a curve could be profitably maintained and would help in the planking-up process of the hull. Also from the viewpoint of usage, the flat 'ram plank' left no protruding keel, a feature which was always susceptible to damage when launching, beaching or in accidentally striking a shoalwater bottom. Functionally, the rockered (convex downward) profile of the 'ram plank' would provide a pivotal centre-point about which the boat could rapidly be turned afloat, but the amount of rocker

4. Michael Rockwood's rescue off Memel probably involved one of the region's high-ended fishing boats (a *Heuer*, after W. Rudolph, 1974).

5. A 'yoll' of Stralsund (after a sketch by D. Friedrichs, 1789). The Lawe House gentlemens' term "Norway Yawl" was a generic one, meaning a double-ended, clench-built, open boat of Scandinavian type.

6. Fishing cobles at Cullercoats, near Tynemouth, c.1840. These beach-launched boats undoubtedly influenced the design of the first Greathead-built lifeboat.

5

6

needed careful judgement since an excess would impart a dangerous lack of directional stability – the boat might simply refuse to run straight in rough conditions. As far as can be ascertained, this rockered 'keel' was definitely not a feature of Greathead's initial, and rejected, submission to the committee.

What exactly prompted Greathead's suggestion for the curved 'keel' remains a matter for conjecture, but there must surely have been some fairly persuasive argument behind it in order to obtain Rockwood's and Fairles agreement to this significant change to their own proposals. However, such a feature was certainly not outside contemporary experience with, for example, William Hutchinson himself advising a moderate curvature of keel for merchant ships in order to improve their strength, their ease of "turning motion" and to help prevent[11] "... their bows from being plunged too deep into the sea in bad weather ...", this last lessening "... the vessel's resistance through the water ...". All were characteristics which would be desirable in a lifesaving boat too. The likelihood, though, is that Greathead's suggestion was drawn from small-boat practice rather than large-ship theory. A fairly conclusive clue to this effect is found in W. R. Hail's *Inquiry into the Invention of the Lifeboat* (1806) where, having decried the importance or good effects of such a 'keel' on the seaworthiness of the lifeboat, he justifiably indicated that Greathead can only be said to have applied the curved keel to his boat and not invented it "... since it was a known feature of at least two other boat types.

The first type cited is[12] "... the boat(s) used in the whale fishery (British Whaleboats) ..." where, to suit Hail's particular argument, he considers the curved keel solely as for "... the convenience of launching them more easily among the ice ... not to make them good seaboats ...". Later authors make it quite clear that it was primarily for purposes of manouevrability:

> *"These boats have very little keel, and curve slightly up to the stem and stern-post which, as they rise from the keel, slope outwards (i.e. are raked). The object of this peculiar build is that the boat may turn quickly to the motions of the whale, and enable the boat-steerer with his long oar to sweep clear of the fish (whale) when fastened".*

Since Tyneside had sent ships to the Arctic whale fishery since 1752 (and, as it happens, 1788 proved to be the peak year with twenty ships fitted-out from the river) there can be little doubt that, in addition to Hails himself, both Greathead and some of the committee members would have been well familiar with the nature and characteristics of the whaleboat type.

The second boat type mentioned by Hails, and the manner of its inclusion, offers up more intriguing possibilities:

> *"There is a boat used in the West Indies called a Moses, to bring the produce from shores where there is constant and heavy surf:*

*this vessel has a curved keel, not to render it more fit to keep the
sea, but to facilitate its landing and launching. To this latter (i.e.
the Moses Boat), I am inclined to believe, Mr. Greathead is
indebted for the hint of the curved keel ...".*

Although well known in its areas of operation, the West Indies, the coasts of
the Southern states of colonial America and some of its northern states too,[13]
the Moses Boat seems unlikely to have been as well known in the maritime
communities of the Tyne as it was, say, to those of Bristol or Liverpool with
their thriving West Indies trade. It is clear though that Greathead had travelled
through coastal areas where 'Moses Boats' were a commonplace – Grenada in
the West Indies, the coasts of Florida and Carolina, together with more
northerly areas such as Massachusetts where Moses boats are known to have
been built for use as ships' boats in the eighteenth century. The exact nature of
these colonial Moses Boats remains obscure since despite numerous
newspaper references and some entries in shipbuilder's account books:[14]

*"No lines, sketches, or measurements of Moses boats except length
in some cases, have so far been found for American boats. Yet
because of the highly distinctive shape and name of the Moses
boat, which sets it apart from other small craft, I believe it is safe
to assume that the type as it was built in America did not differ in
any significant way from the type as it was built in Great Britain,
(i.e. for use in the West Indies) and we do know exactly what the
latter were like."*

Astoundingly, "what the latter" were like was a smaller and dumpier relative of
the South Shields lifeboat!

Although only two original builder's plans of these craft survive,[15] their
provenance, alongside evidence from contemporary illustrations, clearly
indicates that they represent typical examples of the Moses Boat of which two
standard versions seem to have been built, the "single" (with a square, transom
stern) and the "double" (double-ended). The superficial resemblance of the
latter to the lifeboat is striking, with: curved keel running into raked, rounded
stems; low waist and high-sheered ends; shallow floors (bottom) with quite
abrupt turn of the bilge; heavy timber-heads for use in mooring alongside
ships; in section the keel (though obviously not a 'ram plank') is, by
contemporary standards, flat rather than vertical. The differences, which
cannot be denied, are chiefly ones which relate to the Moses boats' very
specific West Indies function – the lightering of hogsheads (massive barrels) of
raw sugar out to offlying merchant ships. Thus, Moses Boats were only 16 feet
in length, a size optimised to carry a single hogshead of sugar in a V-shaped
cradle, as against the Shields' lifeboat's 28 feet. Similarly, their underwater hull-
form was much bluffer and more rounded at the ends, a consequence of their

short overall length and the requirement for sheer carrying-capacity as against speed or ease of propulsion. Though the evidence for the influence of the Moses Boat upon the design of the lifeboat remains circumstantial, there is a clear inference in the wording of Hail's comments that his knowledge of this rather obscure type, and the nature of its "curved keel", derived from the talk of Henry Greathead himself.

As to the overall form of the lifeboat itself, as built in the autumn of 1789, this is also best considered directly from the words of the builder himself. His written description for prospective customers at North Shields in 1798[16] was copied almost *verbatim* into subsequent editions of a standard maritime text of the time:[17]

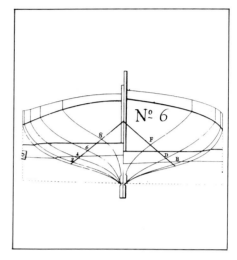

> *"The keel is a plank of three inches thick, of a proportionate breadth in midships, narrowing gradually towards the ends, to the breadth of the stems at the bottom, and forming a great convexity downwards.*
> *The stems are segments of a circle, with considerable rakes. The bottom section, to the floor-heads is a curve fore and aft, with the sweep of the keel.*
> *The floor timber has a small rise curving from the keel to the floor-heads. A bilge plank is wrought in on each side, next the floor-heads, with a double rabbet or groove, of a similar thickness with the keel; and on the outside of this are fixed two bilge-trees, corresponding nearly with the level of the keel.*
> *The ends of the bottom section form that fine kind of entrance observable in the lower part of the bow of the fishing-boat called a coble, much used in the north. From this part to the top of the stem it is more elliptical, forming a considerable projection.*
> *The sides, from the floor-heads to the top of the gunwale, flaunch (flare) off on each side, in proportion to above half the breadth of the floor. The breadth is continued far towards the ends, leaving a sufficient length of straight-side at the top. The sheer is regular along the straight side, and more elevated towards the ends. The gunwale fixed to the outside is three inches thick. The sides, from the under part of the gunwale, along the whole length of the regular sheer, extending twenty-one feet six inches, are cased with layers of cork to the depth of sixteen inches downwards; and the thickness of this casing of cork being four inches it projects at the top a little without the gunwale. The cork on the outside is secured with thin plate, or slips of copper, and the boat is fastened with copper nails.*
> *The thwarts, or seats, are five in number, double banked; consequently, the boat may be rowed with ten oars.*
> *The side oars are short, with iron tholes and rope gromets, so that*

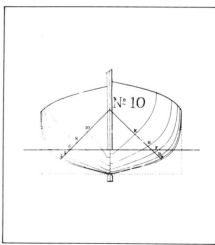

7. Lines plans depicting the double-ended boat types mentioned by Greathead's contemporaries in connection with the origin of the lifeboat; Norway Yawl (top), Whaleboat (bottom), and Moses Boat (overleaf) [from late eighteenth and early nineteenth century sources].

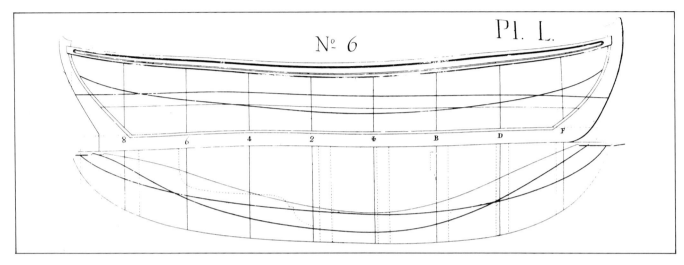

Nº 6 Pl. L.

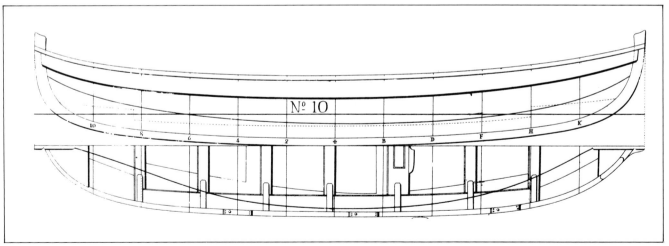

Nº 10

50

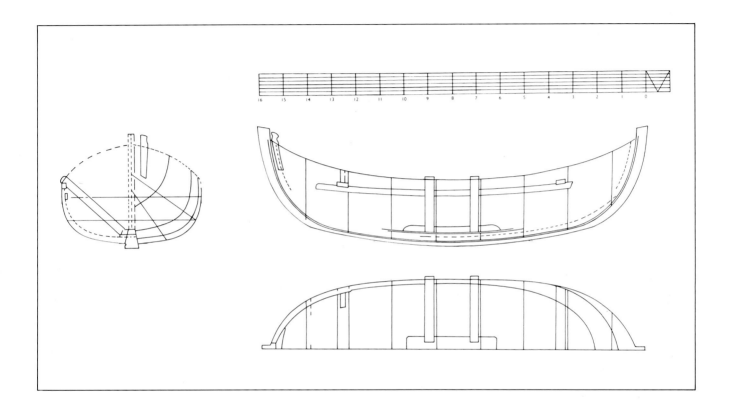

*the rower can pull either way. The boat is steered with an oar at
each end; and the steering oar is one-third longer than the rowing
oar.*

*The platform placed at the bottom, within the boat, is horizontal,
the length of the midships, and elevated at the ends for the
convenience of the steersman, to give him a greater power with
the oar. The internal part of the boat, next the sides, from the
under part of the thwarts down to the platform, is cased with
cork; the whole quantity of which, affixed to the life-boat, is
nearly seven hundred weight.*

The dimensions of this boat were 28 feet 6 inches (8.69m) length by 9 feet
6 inches (2.90m) beam and 3 feet 2 inches (0.96m) depth amidships,
effectively on the proportions of beam as one-third length and depth as one-
third beam. Probably for reasons of cheapness and lightness the hull was
clinker planked (overlapping planks), a technique which also allowed the
builder to produce the characteristics of a "coble bow". By coble standards the
boat's framing was very heavy, using a discontinuous framing system in which
heavy floors (bottom frames) alternated with futtocks (side frames) which also
extended well onto the boat's bottom. This framing, together with the heavy
"bilge planks" (reminiscent of the Viking-ship *meginhufr*, and their external
"bilge-trees" gave massive strength to the boat's bottom and the coble-like
chine at the turn of the bilge. The stems were also of large proportions, with
deep aprons backed by massive, horizontal grown-knees, in addition to the
more usual breasthooks. Judging by his later instructions to boatbuilders
whom he 'licenced' to construct boats of this type, Greathead probably built
the *Original* through a simple sequence of: laying down the 'ram plank' to the
chosen curvature; erecting the stems (whose profiles were simple arcs);
inserting four temporary moulding frames at appropriate distances from the
boat's centre; planking-up to his "rising line" (chine) and fastening in the floor
timbers before continuing with the upper planking and side-frames; finally
followed by fitting-out. Fitting-out included the installation of internal cork
buoyancy and the application of external cork belting under the gunwales.

The disposition and shaping of this cork buoyancy was so close to the
descriptions set-out in Lionel Lukin's "Unimmergible Boat" patent of 1785 that
its inclusion in the Shields lifeboat seems unlikely to have been reached
independently. The form of the external cork belting, in particular, fell well
within the relevant patent specification:[18]

*"... by fitting to the outside of vessels ... projecting gunnells
(gunwales) sloping from the top of the common gunnell in a
faint curve towards the water, so as not to interfere with the oars
in rowing, and from the extreme projection (which may be*

*greater or less, according to the size and the use which the boat or
vessel is intended for) returning to the side in a faint curve at a
suitable height above the waterline. These projecting gunnells
may be solid, of any light material that will not absorb water, or
hollow and watertight, or of cork and covered with thin wood,
canvas, tin or other light metal, mixture or composition. The
projections are very small at the stem and stern and increase
gradually to the dimensions required."*

Lukin's work had, he said, through the "... publication of my patent ... and
(through) advertisements in the public papers, brought the subject ... into very
general discussion at home and abroad". The existence of such recent
publicity, allied to the activities of Archdeacon Sharp in the region in 1788-89
(regarding Lukin's modification of a coble), strongly suggest that the
committee and Greathead were indeed aware of Lukin's work. However, any
acknowledgement of the influence of Lukin's design would have been
tantamount to admitting an infringement of his still current patent!

Whereas Lukin had suggested the use of cork (in conjunction with external
ballast) to resist capsize, for Greathead this was a secondary rather than a
primary function:[19]

> *"The cork fix'd on the outside in the first place is a most excellent
> fender, and with that on the inside above the platform in case the
> boat should be filled with water ... becomes buoyant and prevents
> her upsetting."*

Additionally, he said, the cork belting helped "spread" the water and prevent it
entering the boat when plunging into waves. Popularly the boat's success was
attributed to the cork, and on shore it quickly became known as "the cork
boat", a phrase which, interestingly, Captain John Blackett had used in 1788
when describing Lukin's boat to Sharp. It also became known to some as
"Willie Wouldhave's cork boat", though on objective grounds this title would
now seem difficult to substantiate.

Regrettably, little is known of this enigmatic character William Wouldhave
(or Woodhave, 1751-1821) who had also put a model before the Committee.
He was probably born in North Shields[20], but had long been resident in South
Shields where he apparently followed many trades, gaining a reputation as a
somewhat mercurial and outspoken character with a gift for inventions. He is
said to have:[21]

> *"... suggested an improvement in the building of docks ... weighed
> up a ship which had been sunk and abandoned at the mouth of
> the harbour ... (and) constructed various curious instruments,
> amongst which were an organ, a clock, and an electric machine."*

8. This, the finest contemporary naval
architectural drawing of a Greathead-built
lifeboat was prepared for the Swedish Navy.
In Britain, drawings and sketches were
published in Falconer, 1816, and Steele, 1822.

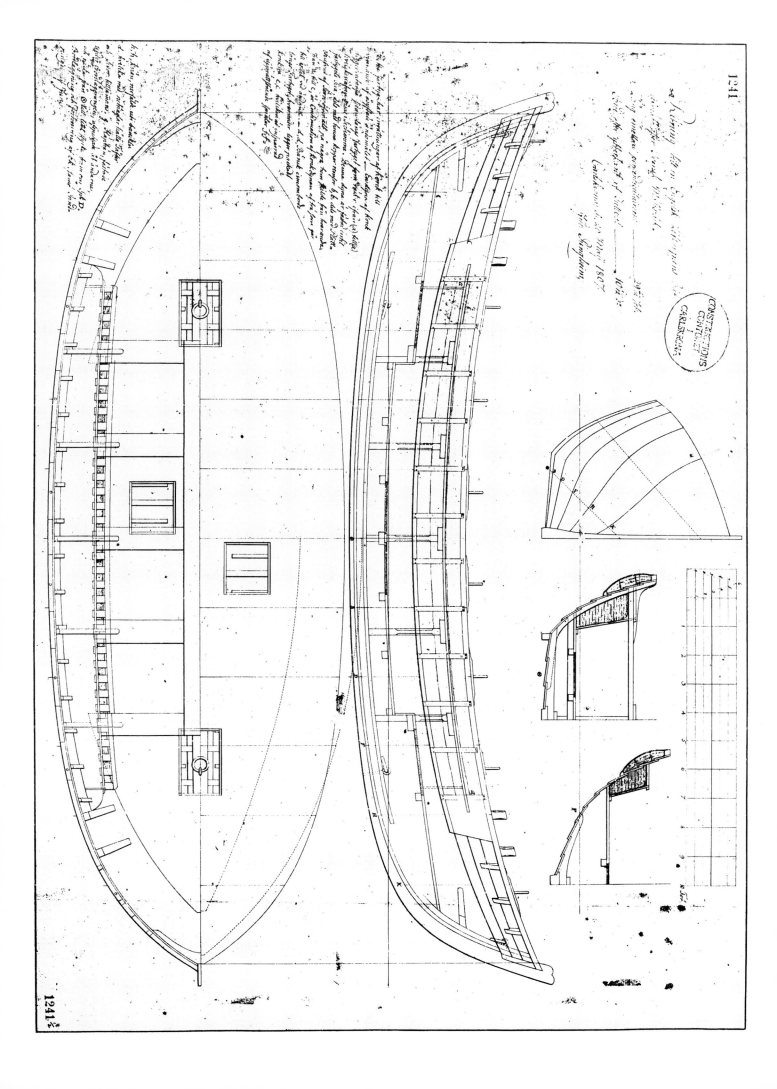

Though the model which he presented in response to the committee's advertisement had been an ingenious one there are, on comparative design grounds, no features which link it indisputably with the boat built by Greathead in 1789. It is true that both Wouldhave's model and this new boat incorporated cork buoyancy but, as has already been shown, this suggestion was hardly unique to Wouldhave. More importantly, Wouldhave's cork had been positioned mainly in end-cases, intended both to resist capsize and to provide for recovery should capsize occur. This feature was not copied into the open-ended, Greathead-built boats. These were not intended to self-right but to resist capsize through their stable hull-form, aided to a lesser extent by the external cork belting. As later events tragically proved, if such boats were capsized they stayed inverted. The fact that both Wouldhave's model and the new lifeboat were double-ended and had considerable sheer (curve at top edge) almost certainly resulted from parallelism of form rather than plagiarism, any practical examination of the functions the boat would have to perform being likely to tend towards the same conclusion.

On the matter of plagiarism, one unsettled issue does remain; this relates to theory rather than practice. Wouldhave is popularly recorded as having discovered his self-righting principle by empirical means, noticing the behaviour of[22] " ... half a circular wooden dish ..." floating in a woman's 'skeel' (tub) of water. Upon further experimentation he found that whatever position this shape (a quarter section of a hollow sphere) was placed in, it always righted itself to a concave-upwards position. This principle, based upon a "spheroidal" section's properties, was then said to have been the basis of his model's self-righting design. Strangely, Greathead also used the term "spheroidal" to describe the properties of the new lifeboat, writing even as early as 1798 that:[23]

> *"... her (the lifeboat's) plan is spheriodically (sic) her motion in the sea from the projection causing a curvature of resistance spreading those waves to the side which comes into other Boats."*

His full, verbal statement on this occasion induced one of those present to write that:[24]

> *"His definition of the boat on mathematical principles, gave great satisfaction to all present ..."*

Four years later, in 1802, Greathead's explanation to the Parliamentary Committee had become more elaborate and, in substance, equated to that attributed to Wouldhave:[25]

> *"... he (Greathead) stated that the following idea had frequently occurred to him, from which he had conceived, the principle of*

his invention; viz. take a spheroid, and divide it into quarters,
each quarter is eliptical, and nearly resembles the half of a wood
bowl, having a curvature with projecting ends; this, thrown into
the sea or broken water, cannot be upset, or lie with the bottom
upwards."

This, on the face of it, would seem to be a clear case of Greathead borrowing
Wouldhave's theory in order to boost his own "invention". But the curious fact
remains that Wouldhave's surviving model does not really illustrate the
development of the quarter spheroid form, whilst the Greathead-built lifeboat,
with its curved keel, does.

However, whatever influences and elements of copying may or may not
have been involved, the most important fact was that the Shields committee
had obtained a boat purposely-designed to attend wrecks at the entrance to
the Tyne. Its final form certainly owed much to a boatbuilder who, probably
justifiably, claimed to have "... been always devoted to marine architecture, a
study which I had cultivated since my infancy". But, as was consistently stated
by Fairles himself, the boat's design was a polyglot one, as well summarised by
the pseudonymous letter-writer "A Son of Tyne" (probably one of the Lawe
House Gentlemen), in 1803:[26]

"... To nautical men, some idea of the form of the boat may be
conveyed by saying, that the top, or upper part of the boat exactly
resembles that of a Memel (east Baltic) fishing boat; the stem and
stern are like those of a Norway Yawl; and the bottom like that of
a Shields coble, having a curved keel superadded"

9. This model, of the lifeboat built for Bawdsey
   (Suffolk) in 1801, probably came from
   Greathead's own workshop and clearly
   illustrates the hull-form and construction of
   the type (note – 'gangboard' missing).

Chapter Five
Early Use and Development

Although apparently ready in the autumn of 1789 the first recorded service of the new boat was not until January 30th 1790, following which this brief account appeared in the *Newcastle Courant*:[1]

> *"We hear from Shields, that the boat lately built by Mr. Greathead, for the purpose of preserving the crews of ships coming on the Herdsand, was first tried out on Saturday last, and far exceeded the expectations of those who had the most sanguine hopes of her utility, for, in going off three times to a vessel then onshore, through a very heavy sea, she scarce shipped any water, and rendered the crew infinite service – we have the satisfaction to add that the sailors present were extremely ready in offering themselves upon the occasion."*

This no doubt was a vital success for, judging by later experience elsewhere, any initial problems with the boat would have been followed by at best its neglect and at worst by outright derision. Indeed, those who gained this immediate, positive publicity – including probably Greathead himself – played an important part in ensuring the new boat's, long-term acceptance. Although detailed records have not survived, it does appear that over the next eight years this South Shields boat was called out regularly and successfully, especially during the winter months.[2] But, by 1797, the demands on the *Institution* which had been formed to support it were outstripping resources. In December of that year, following an exceptionally bad period of ship losses, the original Lawe House committee issued a public appeal for funding to help maintain the boat and pay the crew[3]. They stressed that:

> *"... two hundred persons (have) been brought ashore from ships in distress ..."* but, regrettably, shortage of finance often meant that *".... the men who hazard their lives, in going off to the ships in distress (have) been frequently rewarded by the sufferers themselves ..."*

There was also urgent need for a second boat. This would not only provide for those occasions when more than one ship required assistance, but would promote both a degree of rivalry when going off to wrecks and an element of mutual support in times of danger. Though this appeal elicited some public support, the greatest effect was achieved by the advancement of aristocratic patronage by Hugh Percy, second Duke of Northumberland. He, reputedly, had witnessed the action of the South Shields lifeboat when saving the crew of the *Planter* in late November 1797.[4] In any event, on the 30th January 1798 his formal offer to contribute towards a new lifeboat was conveyed to the "... members of a subscription coffee-room we have near Dockwray Square (North Shields) ...". Here, under John Walker, then leading citizen of North Shields,

1. The Storm, scene at Tynemouth, Northumberland, by T. M. Richardson, 1827. To the right, the *Northumberland* lifeboat is being manhandled down to the beach.

2. The remarkable Greathead-built lifeboat *Zetland*; active on the Redcar (Cleveland) station 1801-1880, credited with saving hundreds of lives and still preserved today.

these men set up their own committee, advertised in the Newcastle newspapers and called a public meeting on the 8th February at the George Tavern, in order to establish "... a CORK or LIFE BOAT in North Shields." Walker's intention was that Greathead should build the North Shields boat and, following Greathead's attendance at the meeting, his proposals were forwarded to the Duke for approval. Greathead suggested one improvement in particular over the South Shields boat, the coppering (copper-plating) of the new boat's bottom, recommending that it should:[5]

> "... be coppered as high as the floorheads. It will take 250 feet of square copper one pound weight to a square foot which with the composition nails ... and additional cork will amount to 20 or 30 pounds (money). It will be observed that Boats built to be coppered should be copper fastened, the nails and bolts for that purpose will make a difference of £10."

He added that:

> "... Sir John Swinburne was lately looking at the boat alluded to (the South Shields Boat) and greatly approved of the plan ...".

Walker's own estimate of cost, £50, was immediately corrected by Greathead, who pointed out that the South Shields boat had cost £75 eight years previously, and higher materials costs alone would now increase that to £100; that total would be raised to £130-£140 by the suggestion of "coppering". However, the pragmatic Walker still:[6]

> "... recommend(ed) strenuously to Your Grace, that the same person (Greathead) might be permitted to build the intended boat as it is probable (that) the same confidence in cases of emergency, might not be placed on any other (builder), as I find the construction of the bottom is a most essential matter as well as the cork ...".

So, Walker at least recognised that the lifeboat's hull-form was its primary asset, with the cork acting only as a contributory factor. Much to his embarrassment, the new boat, at £159-4s-0d, cost even more than his revised estimate to the Duke. It was longer by two feet and broader than anticipated, and in Walker's absence elsewhere he felt that Greathead:[7] "... may have presumed too much on Clark's (one of Walker's colleagues) ingenuity and perhaps charged too extravagant ...", but admitted that Greathead had been "importuned" by Sir John Swinburne and the North Shields' committee to produce a boat that should be "... as compleat as possible ... and of the best materials."
Greathead's explanations seem genuine enough:

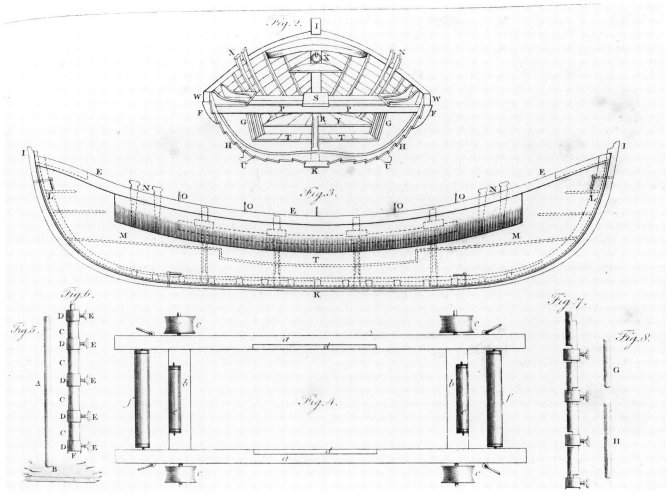

3. This contemporary plan of a Greathead
lifeboat clearly shows the type's construction,
including: the curved, flat-sectioned keel (K);
strengthening 'bilge-trees' (U); external cork
belting (F); internal cork buoyancy (G);
heavy platform flooring (T, M); and well-
braced rowing thwarts (P). Below (Figs. 14-
81) is Greathead's rather controversial rail-
borne launching carriage.
(from Falconer's *Marine Dictonary*, 1816).

> *"... my mind being continually employed in improvement, after selecting the best materials at the highest prices. I have secured the bottom below the platform with a Kelson fore and aft the length of the Keel, with Rider Timbers and the Platform laid with a Deal thicker than I first proposed, and laid in such a manner as only to require a light caulking ... the copper and copper nails both exceeded my estimate ... I have made the drift bolts and Rowlocks copper with a greater proportion of copper to secure the cork. The cork I have doubled in proportion to what I suggested ... being convinced that in the case of her bottom being stove, the proportion of cork will swim her ...".*

Actually, these intentions had been pointed out in advance to the North Shields committee by Greathead together with the reasons for them, the danger of the hull being damaged from above or below:[8]

> *"... the platform (internal floor) secur'd and made tight and fill'd underneath with Cork, as a counterpoise to that the boats bottom on the outside up to be Coppered. The advantage I propose from this is the boat is most likely to be stove up aloft by the fall of mast etc. from the wreck. The Boat so stove might be conducted ashore again by the people, the wind and sea in those cases always bearing upon the Shore. If in her motion she should strike against the wreck with her bottom the Copper is ductile not easy breaking as wood, which with the platform being tight and secur'd would form a second bottom."*

Though it could be argued that Greathead's suggestion of "coppering" derived from Wouldhave's proposal for an all-metal (copper) boat the more likely explanation seems to be Greathead's familiarity with the relatively new technique of "coppering" (for protection from marine-borers) as practiced in the Navy. In his memoirs, he notes his former ship the *Vulture* as being "... I believe, the first vessel on which that operation was ever performed in America". He must have participated in this process for on 8th June 1781, the ship's log[9] notes that they "... Hove (the) keel out, the Carpenters employed Coppering the larboard side and the Bottom."

This new Greathead-built boat, named the *Northumberland* in honour of her patron, was soon in service, earning not only local but also national publicity for her first rescue on the 16th November 1798, saving the crew of the sloop *Edinburgh*. From this time onwards these two boats, *Original* and *Northumberland*, under the control of the Tyne Lifeboat Institution, achieved great distinction, saving hundreds of lives under the most arduous and dangerous of conditions.[10] Oddly, because they were so successful and durable they proved to be the only two Greathead-built boats to be used by the Tyne

4. A public notice of 1823. Lifeboat management did not always run smoothly — boats were misused, payments improperly accepted and shipowner's avoided making contributions.

NORTHUMBERLAND
Life Boat.

WHEREAS the BOAT HOUSE DOOR, has of late been repeatedly broken open, and the Boat taken away, without the sanction of the Committee, at same time leaving the House open, and thereby exposing the Boat's Stores to pilferage, in order to put a stop to such Outrageous proceedings, the Committee are determined to punish any Person or Persons found guilty of such Conduct in future.

The Committee also determine, that the Crew who may go off with the Boat, shall on their return moor the Boat, and at a proper Time of the Tide, assist in getting her into the House, and in order to have the Expence of the Boat going off amicably settled, Persons liable to pay, are requested not to settle with any Person, without a written Order for the same, signed by two of the acting Committee.

A KEY of the BOAT HOUSE DOOR is lodged with the TIDE SURVEYORS, at the CUSTOM HOUSE WATCH HOUSE, and the Boat will be in constant readiness, to go off in all cases of Danger, to save the Lives of Shipwrecked Mariners, and for no Purpose whatever.

SHIP-OWNERS are respectfully reminded, that any Ship which has not contributed TEN SHILLINGS AND SIXPENCE to the Fund of the Life Boat, since such Ship became their Property, are liable to pay the whole Expence of the Boat going off (about EIGHT POUNDS) should such Assistance be necessary.

Donations and Subscriptions

will be received by Mr JAMES BURNE, Treasurer; also by the acting COMMITTEE at NORTH SHIELDS; or at the CUSTOM-HOUSE, NEWCASTLE.

JOHN HUTCHINSON
WILLIAM REAY
MILES HANN
ROBERT YOUNG } ACTING COMMITTEE.

North Shields, March 12, 1823.

Lifeboat Institution. The *Original* eventually suffered irreparable damage in 1830 and the *Northumberland* was sold after damage around 1846. For a further century, though, this independent lifesaving Institution continued to use modified forms of the Greathead-built type of boat, whose characteristics seemed best suited to their own local requirements – beach launching for relatively short trips through severe, shallow-water surf conditions. Such boats' characteristics were well explained by the builder himself:[11]

> *"The curving keel and bottom admits a boat to be much easier winded and is of moment in the trough of the sea and is also much easier steered, the great rake of the stems, with the fine entrance below forming part of the Coble Bow, the construction of the Coble Bow is beyond all others for making its way thro the Sea ... The Breath (sic) of the Boat being carried well towards the ends hath this advantage, those Boats whose extream breath lays well forward have been found by experience to be the best sea boats for rowing against it. In very high seas it is always attended with danger ... to wear or lay across the Sea, both ends of the boat being built alike either end goes forward. So wearing (turning around) may very often be prevented ... when the Boat has obtain'd the wreck she may be row'd back again without winding (turning) the thofts & thouls (thwarts and thole pins) are so placed that the men by turning themselves round may row ashore again, the steer oar from the other end ... From her fine entrance at the end below. The great rake of the Stem the projection of the Bow, lifts the Boat up almost perpendicular. The Sea breaking as she goes over it. The other end from the same form is lifted up and she launches over it with great velocity ..."*

Greathead's emphasis on the "Coble Bow" and the boat's ability to lift over shoreline surf was not accidental. These were characteristics which the boats' crews, chiefly composed of coble-using Tyne Pilots, were most familiar with and would demand of any boat that they were to man. Indeed, the success of the boat lay quite literally in the hands of these "Pilots of Tinmouth Haven" whom Hutchinson himself had reckoned were "... the best and most dexterous (men) for working and managing ships in crowded, narrow or dangerous channels ... (they) are more expert than other people I have seen ...". Their profession was strictly regulated and confined to members of long-established families. And, though coming under the overall jurisdiction of Trinity House, Newcastle, efforts were then being made by one of the Gentlemen of the Lawe House, William Blackburn, to apply some local control through a mutual

5. Of the early illustrators, the local artist Luke Clenell (1781-1840) best captured the pioneering spirit and courage of the Pilots manning the new Life-Boats.

Benefit Society. But even the sympathetic Blackburn admitted that this tough and independent group of men were "... a strange Set of unruly Fellows...".[12] Unruly by his standards perhaps, but undoubtedly showing the highest levels of seamanship and bravery in their home waters, and maybe to be forgiven if occasionally the use of the lifeboat extended to salvage as well as rescue.[13]

6. Made by Stephen Laverick, one of Greathead's apprentices, this lifeboat model has long hung in St. Hilda's Church, South Shields. Such 'votive ship-models' are quite rare in Britain.

PILOTS' SOCIETY,
South Shields.

ADDITIONAL ARTICLES.

At the Annual Meeting held January 24th, 1794.

RESOLVED,

That the Guardians may reduce the Contributions, of the Members *advanced in Years*, (tho' working.) till they come on the Fund, for Relief.

At the Annual Meeting, held January 26th, 1795.

RESOLVED,

That on and after the 9th Day of March, 1795, (on Account of the Defalcation in the Contributions) the Mode of Payment, directed by the 4th Section of the Articles, shall cease, And instead thereof, every Member shall pay weekly, on Monday in every week, the Sum of one Shilling: And if any Member shall be, at any time, upwards of four Weeks in Arrear, he shall forfeit 5s. If upwards of six Weeks in Arrear, he shall forfeit 10s. And if upwards of Eight Weeks in Arrear, or if he shall refuse to pay the Fines, he shall be excluded. — And that the relief shall be, as heretofore.

By Order of the GUARDIANS, and PILOTS.

WM BLACKBURN, SECRETARY.

7. Tyne Pilots Society handbill, signed by William Blackburn, 1794. His intentions were obviously frustrated by the members' financial laxity!

Chapter Six

Recognition and Failure

Despite their local success and the national notice attendant upon the patronage of the Duke of Northumberland, it seems doubtful if the Shields "Life-Boats" would have achieved further recognition, or more widespread adoption, without the promotional efforts of Henry Greathead himself. Already, whilst building the *Northumberland* he was preparing a model to be sent via some "Newcastle Gentlemen" to the Royal Society of Arts, although it was to be three years before this move proved fruitful. Similarly, models were prepared both for the Duke himself and for Sir John Swinburne, Greathead engaging in correspondence with the latter over suggested improvements to his designs. Locally, Greathead almost certainly played a part in supplying rescue stories to the local newspapers. For example the account of the *Edinburgh*, 1798, which appeared successively in the local and national press, his letters, national journals and, finally, in a witness's statement to the Parliamentary Committee of 1802. Indeed his detractors later accused him of self-glorification in such use of the press, whose reports often featured his name and sometimes his actions.

Greathead's relationship with Swinburne (1762-1860), however, was certainly a much more important factor. Swinburne was not only related by marriage to the Duke of Northumberland, but through the latter's interest had gained a parliamentary seat in 1788. Within the region he was elected High Sheriff of Northumberland in 1799 and was especially noted for his

1. Henry Greathead c.1804, (1757-c.1816) and three of the major participants in the events which led to his recognition as "the inventor of the lifeboat"

Sir John Swinburne (1762-1860)

Rowland Burdon, M.P. (1756-1838)

Hugh Earl Percy, Second Duke of Northumberland (1742-1817)

humanitarian and intellectual interests, presiding for forty years over "... the fortunes of the Newcastle Literary and Philosophical Society...", and for fifty over the Newcastle Society of Antiquaries. By the standards of the time he was regarded as "... a model of a country gentleman, a kind and liberal landlord, an open-handed contributor to local charities[1]..." whose attitudes towards his Northumberland tenants reflected[2] "... a just model of old English hospitality, a true characteristic of the Swinburne family." It was not until 1801, however, that Greathead was able to use his connection with Swinburne to the full. In 1800 Greathead had secured his first 'outside' order for a lifeboat, through a noted St. Andrews citizen, Cathcart Dempster, and by April 1801 he was able to inform Swinburne[3] that he had now built boats for Lowestoft (Suffolk), Bawdsey Haven (Suffolk) and St. Andrews (Fife), whilst another was under construction for Montrose (Forfarshire) and there were also enquiries from the safety-conscious Port of Dublin.[4] Through this last contact Greathead was made aware that the need for a national lifeboat service was about to be raised at governmental level, by the Marquis of Hertford and Pitt in the House of Lords. The former had sought the support of the Duke of Northumberland in order to[5] "... extend the benefit of the life Boats which your Grace first countenanced and introduced to the Public, from the Northern Ports to London ..." and he had also contacted the local gentry responsible for establishing a Greathead-built lifeboat at Lowestoft. Sadly, owing to a fall of government, the Marquis' plans were not progressed further, though it had been his intention "... to bring forward Mr. Greathead in consequence of your Grace's recommendations."

After this setback Greathead decided to pursue his case for recognition and reward personally. He placed the matter first before the Newcastle Literary and Philosophical Society in May of 1801, presumably with their President Sir John Swinburne's agreement. This Society formally endorsed his claims and transmitted them to Rowland Burdon (1756-1838), the Member of Parliament for Sunderland.[6] Burdon was a man whom a later biographer described as "... being raised above mere party ties (through) his philanthropy, public spirit and integrity ...", and he had previously shown sympathetic concern for seamen's affairs.[7] By September, he had indicated his support for Greathead's claim to the "invention" of the lifeboat, and Greathead was hopeful that Charles Grey (later Earl Grey), an M.P. for Northumberland would second the petition.

Burdon soon made representations to the Duke of Northumberland and Lord St. Vincent (First Lord of the Admiralty), presenting the latter with a lifeboat model which is still in existence. Meanwhile, a descriptive account of the lifeboat, culled from a Royal Society report of 1800, had gained general public notice in the widely-circulated, radical *Monthly Magazine*. But at local level, Greathead's approaches were meeting a mixed reception. John Walker of North Shields readily supplied information to support the case which Burdon would present through a petition to Parliament, but to Swinburne he more realistically wrote that:[8]

> *"... he (Greathead) is too sanguine in his expectations of*
> *obtaining any Gratuity from the Admiralty or Navy Board, tho'*
> *he most assuredly deserves some reward for his ingenuity."*

The Lawe House committee members were even more circumspect when approached by Greathead in October 1801 with a request that they sign a certificate naming him as the "inventor" of the lifeboat. Eventually they certified a text (recommended by Fairles) which considerably qualified this claim, stating only that:[9]

> *"... Mr. Henry Greathead, of South Shields, Boatbuilder, did deliver*
> *in a model of a boat for that purpose (lifesaving); and from his*
> *design and explanations being most satisfactory ... he was*
> *selected to build the first boat, which is on the flaunching plan;*
> *and that the curved-keel, which is the principal difference of this*
> *boat from any other on that plan, is, in our opinion, the reason of*
> *her answering beyond every expectation ... and that such curved*
> *keel is the original invention and idea of the said Henry*
> *Greathead ... 29th October, 1801".*

Though undersigned by Heath, Masterman, Roxby and Marshall (Rockwood was probably indisposed or deceased) of the original committee, together with twenty surviving Lawe House subscribers (including Blackburn), Nicholas Fairles still refused to sign. His reason, indicated to Burdon, was that[10] "... I could not do it consistent with the truth".

Such a *caveat* however was unlikely to restrain a campaign which had now gained a momentum of its own—reputations were beginning to ride on the "invention of the lifeboat". A laudatory letter by a prominent Scarborough citizen, Thomas Hinderwell, was received by Greathead for local publication in November 1801.[11] Its text was soon used to good effect in a submission to the Royal Humane Society (December 1801), and then through Trinity House (London) to obtain a lifeboat order from the Trustees of Ramsgate Harbour. Hinderwell also obtained support from Lord Mulgrave and William Wilberforce, and he later acted as an eloquent witness for Greathead before the Parliamentary Committee.

Metropolitan recognition was now imminent. After two years of disinterest, the Royal Humane Society decided, in December 1801, to present Greathead with their Honorary Medallion and by the end of the following month the Society of Arts and Manufactures had followed with the choice "... of a medal or a pecuniary award". Greathead chose the latter though in the event he received both 50 guineas and a gold medal. The Elder Brethren of Trinity House, London, were meanwhile considering a recommendation by one of their members, Captain Gilfrid Reed, that they should "... offer the testimony of their great satisfaction at this invention ...". This testimony was made real in

2. Two of the models mentioned by Greathead:
the functional model sent to London and
eventually presented to Lord St. Vincent (First
Lord of the Admiralty), and the rather
decorative model placed before the
Parliamentary Committee of 1802 (from the
collections of the National Maritime
Museum).

May 1802 by the donation of 100 guineas as a reward for Greathead's ingenuity in constructing the "Life-Boat", and for the "... benefits rendered by this valuable invention." The award was a little surprising in view of the fact that Reed was in charge of the Lowestoft lifeboat. This boat had been emphatically rejected by the local beachmen as unsafe for use on their coast,[12] a failure which Greathead put down (rightly or wrongly) to the "... prejudice of the Salvage Men"[13], However, Reed also acted as a very positive witness for Greathead before the Parliamentary Committee.

Greathead's Parliamentary petition was presented in the House of Commons on the 25th February 1802,[14] by Rowland Burdon M.P., with the secondment of the reformer William Wilberforce M.P. (for Hull) who had supported Burdon on maritime matters before. Having first given the background to the development of the lifeboat, Greathead petitioned on the grounds that:

> "... your Petitioner, having thus been instrumental in saving the lives of so many persons; and the utility of the Boat being now established; and your petitioner having derived little or no pecuniary advantage whatever from the invention, his models having been made public: – He humbly hopes that this Honourable House will take his case into their consideration, and grant your Petitioner such reward, as to this Honourable House shall seem meet."

There was, significantly, no claim to the Boat's "invention". The petition was immediately referred for consideration by a large Parliamentary Committee containing a number of north-east men and others drawn from coastal counties. Their terms of reference were drawn up to:

> "...direct their inquiries particularly to the three following subjects:
> First; The Utility of the Life-Boat:
> Secondly; The Originality of the Invention claimed by Mr. Greathead:
> Thirdly; Whether he had received any, and what, Remuneration."

The Committee examined eight witnesses in addition to Greathead himself. Not surprisingly all eight gave favourable accounts of the lifeboat's performances, and instanced rescues which had been carried out. With respect to the lifeboat's originality, especial attention was paid to its possible derivation from the "Norway Yawl". Four witnesses were questioned in this respect: a north-east coast seaman, a Newcastle shipmaster, an elderly Shields ship master and Captain Reed of Trinity House, London. All confirmed that the lifeboat was significantly different to the "Norway Yawl", in particular having greater sheer

3. These laudatory verses, dedicated to Henry Greathead in 1802, were later used to good effect in his publicity campaign. The 'poet', the humanitarian Dr. Thomas Trotter, was amongst the Navy's first reforming physicians, and settled in Newcastle upon retirement.

4. This contemporary model represents the lifeboat built by Chas. Smith of Scarborough, 1801, from a plan supplied by Henry Greathead. Under the auspices of Scarborough's noted townsman, Thomas Hinderwell, and crewed by local fishermen, it carried out many dangerous rescues (from the Scarborough Rotunda Museum Collection).

and the ability to work in shoal water. Captain Reed was questioned closely on the matter of Lukin's patent and answered that, as a member of the Royal Humane Society, he had seen many impractical lifesaving devices containing cork but had no memory of Lukin's boat – a rather odd admission. He was also pressed hard on the effectiveness of the Lowestoft lifeboat, but expressed his confidence in this Greathead-built boat, explaining away its lack of use through the local "sailors" lack of experience with it.

Of the eight witnesses called, two had intimate knowledge of the lifeboat's origins and use in Shields, (Sir) Cuthbert Heron, who had witnessed the loss of the *Adventure* in 1789, and William Masterman, one of the original Lawe House committee. Both men had signed Greathead' s "Certificate of Invention" in October 1801, which they now ratified before the Parliamentary Committee. When examined himself, Greathead made clear claim "... to be the inventor of the Life-Boat ...", indicating that this invention had resulted from:

> *"... a premium (being) offered by the Ship owners and inhabitants of South Shields, for the construction of a boat for the peculiar purpose of saving shipwrecked mariners. He was therefore induced to offer a model; which being approved, he was employed to build a boat from it. That model was similar to the model before your (Parliamentary) committee ...".*

This statement can be regarded either as an outright lie – for his initial model was clearly rejected by the Lawe House committe – or it may have been a distorted version of the truth. For Greathead definitely had made another model for the Lawe House committee. This model, which represented the first lifeboat built, is clearly referred to in his correspondence of 1798.[15] Tantalisingly, there is no clear evidence as to when exactly this model was made, whether before or after the *Original's* actual construction.

In any event the Parliamentary Committee did not seriously query Greathead's claim as "inventor" or "discoverer" of the "Life-Boat", and neither did they dispute his lack of remuneration for building these boats. They accepted his statement that profits per boat were in the region of £10 to £15 (on a craft costing some £165). For even less than £5 'licences' had been granted to build "Life- Boats" elsewhere, no attempt having been made to enforce exclusivity by patenting the design. Their conclusions on this subject seem reasonable since, to date, Greathead had profited from the building of only seven boats and the 'licencing' of three or four over a period of a dozen years. Frustratingly for Greathead, Parliamentary procedure then delayed consideration of the Committee's findings from the 31st March until the 2nd June, when, after some sharp debate over the sum to be awarded, a compromise payment of £1200 was made:

> *"... as a reward for his Invention of the Life-Boat, whereby many*

*lives have already been saved, and great security is afforded to
seamen and property, in cases of Shipwreck."*

During the debate it was revealed that Greathead's stay in London to prosecute
his petition had cost between £100 and £200 but that by way of compensation
this period had also "... been the means of introducing him to several bodies,
who might forward him in the way of his business."

One such body, Lloyds of London, had already taken measures which
benefited Greathead directly through the award of 100 guineas, and indirectly
through the establishment of a fund of £2,000 to "... encourage the building of
LIFE-BOATS, on different parts of the coasts of these Kingdoms."[16] Lloyds'
actions in May 1801, may have been hastened by their impression that
Greathead's Parliamentary petition might fail. Significantly, Greathead was not
altogether a newcomer to this prestigious establishment. His contact there

5. The Coffee Room at Lloyds, 1798. A rather
impious view of the institution whose name
became synonymous with fidelity in
insurance and worldwide maritime trade.

reached back over twenty years, to that time in his career when in 1778 he was 'wrecked' on the coast of France. His deliberately inconclusive biographical notes about this event (which omitted the ship's name) actually obscured the fact that:[17]

> "... as a ship's carpenter he (had) assisted in detecting a peculiarly impudent case of fraudulent stranding ..."

This had saved a major underwriter, Mr. Peter Warren (now partner to Julius Angerstein, the 'father-figure' of Lloyds) and his subscribers, a considerable loss. This service was now repaid both in cash and, perhaps more importantly, in status through their giving Greathead unquestioning credit for the "invention" of the lifeboat. Whether or not Greathead had received any previous reward for his action in 1778 is not clear, but if so it might help to explain his ability to set-up in business following his discharge from the Navy. Lloyds' support for Greathead may of course have had a wider element of self-interest too. The establishment of a network of lifeboat stations would almost certainly prevent some genuine loss of (insured) ships and merchandise, and might also help discourage the fraudulent loss of vessels, a particular cause of concern to underwriters of the period.

Greathead's success in obtaining both a Parliamentary award and public endorsement by the two leading maritime organisations of the day (Lloyds and Trinity House, London) was in no small measure due to his own self-belief and persistence. Although only from a tradesman's background, it is evident from his surviving letters that, if not a 'gentleman' himself, he was able to order and present his ideas with clarity whilst at the same time adopting that level of respect (though never servility) which was expected from one in his social position. But these abilities alone would seem insufficient to explain the success of what was, after all, a fairly ordinary and disputable claim for reward from the public purse. Circumstances favoured him locally in the pro-active response of a member of the Northumbrian gentry, Sir John Swinburne, whose family connections led directly to an aristocratic patron, Hugh Duke of Northumberland, who possessed not only metropolitan influence but, quite unusually, a technical and personal knowledge of seafaring too. The goodwill of a local Member of Parliament with maritime interests, Rowland Burdon, then provided the route by which to progress his petition. Luckiest chance of all was Greathead's opportunity to exploit London circles through his purely fortuitous service to Lloyds twenty years previously. Maybe one further, unspoken but accepted factor helped smooth Greathead's way. In 1787 he was elected secretary of the St. Hild's Lodge of Freemasons (est. 1780), and he subsequently held further offices within the lodge.[18] Both Swinburne, who became Provincial Grand Master in 1807, and Burdon were noted members of this then regionally expanding organisation.[19]

The publicity and recognition afforded to Greathead following the

Parliamentary Reward, and those awards which had immediately preceded it, resulted in an immediate upsurge of demand for lifeboats. In the preceding two years, he had built only five, but output for 1802 alone now rose to ten and reached a peak in 1803 when no less than fourteen were built, six of which were for stations abroad.[20] Immediately following the Parliamentary decision he issued the now famous engraving, by Elmes of London, depicting "the lifeboat going to a wreck" with a dedication to the Duke of Northumberland and caption announcing himself as "inventor of the Life-Boat". By June of 1802 he was having to advertise for additional boatbuilders to meet demand, and two months later was issuing warnings to intending purchasers to beware of imitations of his product.[21] This, however, was not the only problem which came with fame and fortune, for in July 1802 the *Monthly Magazine* published an anonymous letter repudiating his claim to be the inventor of the lifeboat. This potentially damaging controversy proved to be short-lived; regrettably, the boom in lifeboat building also proved to be short-lived.

With the immediate requests for lifeboats satisfied and the nation pre-occupied with European strife the demand for Greathead's boats fell

6. This "... large and elegant Print of the Life-Boat, invented by Mr. Henry Greathead, of South Shields ..." was dedicated to the Duke of Northumberland and formed part of Greathead's publicity campaign following the 1802 Parliamentary Award. The engraving (by Elmes of London) was after a painting by Newcastle artist Joseph Atkinson, which was to be exhibited at "... all the principal Seaports in Great Britain."

drastically. In the six years from 1804 to 1810 he produced a total of only nine lifeboats for service on British and foreign stations. If his boatbuilding establishment had been increased to meet the demands of 1802-03 it was still presumably not a large one. A government survey of 1805 records his yard as having only "one man below 50 years of age (presumably Greathead himself) and three apprentices", compared to the two men and five apprentices of his long-established South Shields competitors, Olivers.[22] Two of Greathead's apprentices, though, Stephen Laverick and George Farrow, were to achieve special note, with the latter entering award-winning lifeboat designs in local and national competitions in the 1840s and 1850s. Unfortunately, surviving records give no hint as to the other open boats built by Greathead's yard, though in the period 1796-1806 he did build two larger, decked vessels; the clinker-built, 36-ton cutter *North Creak*, 1790, and the small, 129-ton brig *Affiance*, 1800.[23]

In 1808, having built only one lifeboat in each of the two previous years, Greathead appears to have attempted to revive the national consciousness and his business once more by re-introducing a proposal he had first published in 1804. His approach this time was made directly to the Lords of the Admiralty, recommending that they adopt lifeboats for shipboard use. This met with a guarded response, since although recognising that the lifeboat[24] "... is well adapted for the service for which it is intended ..." they "... doubt(ed) her fitness for the general purposes of a Ship's Boat ...", although admitting that "... we are aware occasions sometimes occur at Sea when a small Boat constructed on this principle would be very desirable." A decision was taken to order four or five small (25-foot) lifeboats on trial for issue to "... such Flag Ships as shall apply for them in lieu of Jolly Boats (a small ship's boat used for light work)". But Greathead's further suggestion of the Admiralty establishing a chain of lifeboat stations along the coast was firmly rejected by their Lordships:

> "... we apprehend it will not be expedient for Government to order an Establishment which, to be useful must be carried to a great extent and be attended by a heavy expence ...".

At departmental level even the expense of building the five small lifeboats caused officials concern, for it was found that they could not:

> "... agree with him (Greathead) for building the said boats for a less sum than one hundred and eighty pounds each, with two Sliding Keels, and one hundred and seventy pounds without Sliding Keels ...".

Such concern is not surprising, since the Jolly Boats which the lifeboats were intended to replace cost only £11.17s each![25] However, the order was placed in July 1808 and by November three of the boats had arrived at Woolwich, with the other two[26] "... expected to arrive shortly...", a fast piece of work by Greathead. Unfortunately, there is no later record about their use, if any, and no further boats were ordered. The incident though is interesting on two grounds, political and technical. The decision to order the boats was – in terms of cost as against likely function – a rather odd one considering the demands of the times, and the suspicion must be that some 'interest' still remained in London to support Greathead's case. Technically, the offer to provide boats with "Sliding Keels" indicates his continued interest in an innovation first discussed with Sir John Swinburne in 1802.

It may indeed have been Swinburne who first indicated to Greathead the advantages of applying sail-power and keels to the lifeboat. The idea's potential was demonstrated in September 1802,[27] when the new Whitby boat was sailed from the Tyne to Whitby (43 sea miles) in seven hours, using a makeshift rig of two coble lug-sails and jib with one of the steering oars fixed to the aftermost lee thole "... in the manner of a Leeboard ...". Following this success, Greathead proposed an experimental "18-20 foot, sliding keel" boat but this did not mature, though a fine model illustrating his proposals was completed in October 1802.[28] The sliding keels (i.e. daggerboards, centreboards) were quite clearly copied from those first demonstrated in America by Captain Schank R.N. (1774) who subsequently tested them successfully in the Navy's *Trial* cutter (1791), before their adoption in a number of other Naval vessels.[29]

Though Greathead may have learnt directly of Schank's work, it seems much more likely that the information and spur for his proposed adaptation came from a more local and influential source, since:[30]

> "... (Schank's) great ingenuity ... procured him the warmest patronage and friendship of the Duke of Northumberland, who was an eye-witness in America to the great utility of sliding keels ... his Grace is an excellent shipwright, and very fond of all nautical improvements."

Furthermore, it seems that whilst in America the Duke had procured a boat with sliding keels for his own use, and amongst his surviving nautical papers there are documents relating to Schank's work – work which the Duke was instrumental in promoting against established Naval opinion. On this occasion though it proved to be Greathead's ideas which were ahead of their time, since despite the successful conversion of a Suffolk Beach Yawl into a 'lifeboat' in 1807 by his now competitor, Lionel Lukin, the sailing lifeboat with drop keels was not to become an established reality for another 50 years.

The failure to get lifeboats accepted by the Navy as regular equipment for larger ships-of-war, dwindling interest in both lifesaving in general and the establishment of a national service in particular, combined perhaps with difficult trading conditions, seem to have brought Greathead's business into decline. He built only one lifeboat in the two years 1809-10. Although perhaps attempting to diversify – for example, in 1809[31] "... a six oared Greenland Boat (whaleboat) built on the plan of the Lifeboat ..." was sold from an ex Tyne Whaler – it seems likely that the initial success of his "invention" had caused him to depend too heavily on one type of product. Neither can it be ruled out that some of his early monetary rewards had been dissipated unwisely, or that his overt success had resulted in commercial hostility in the locality. In any event, in November 1810, shortly after the death of his mother, he was declared bankrupt:[32]

> *WHEREAS HENRY GREATHEAD, of South Shields, in the County of Durham, Boatbuilder, hath by Assignment, bearing the date of 29th October Instant, assigned all his Estate and Effects unto James Laing, of South Shields aforesaid, Gentleman, in Trust, for the equal benefit of his Creditors, who shall execute the said Assignment in or before the 20th November next ..."*

The censures of local, nineteenth-century historians about this occurrence seem rather harsh:[33, 34]

> *"...it irks me to add, that in spite of a parliamentary grant of £1200 voted to him in 1802, and a hundred guineas from the Trinity House etc., he actually became a bankrupt."*

> *"Yet, strange to say, Mr. Greathead, notwithstanding these grants and the extension of his business, actually became a bankrupt."*

These remarks are particularly hard to reconcile with the same commentators' bare mention of Nicholas Fairles bankruptcy two years later, which involved not only his personal finances but charitable monies too. Through longevity and influence Fairles was, in due course, able to discharge his debts and regain his position, but Henry Greathead "the inventor of the Life-Boat" simply disappeared from view.

Greathead's date of death is generally accepted as 1816, but confirmation of this is not to be found in local records, the likelihood being that by then he had left Shields. This is further suggested by the report of his wife's death in London in March 1814,[35] as the "... wife of Mr. Henry Greathead, formerly of South Shields". Probably they had travelled south to the capital where she had family ties and where he might still hope to restore his own connections and fortunes, and perhaps he did die there in 1816. But in the *Naval Chronicle* of January 1817 there appeared, under the pseudonym of "Alfred",[36] an echo of the Henry Greathead of yesteryear recommending that: following great loss of life from the Naval transport *Harpooner*, Greathead-type lifeboats should be carried by "... all naval vessels of the higher rates and dimensions."

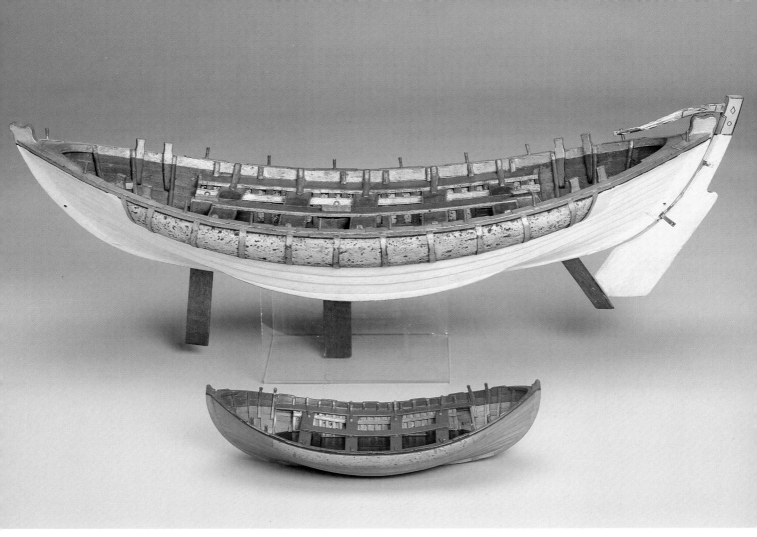

7. Greathead's fine model of a lifeboat fitted with sliding keels and rudder for sailing, together with a small Admiralty-style model which may have represented the 25-foot design of 1808 (from the collections of the National Maritime Museum).

Conclusion

Although his last years may have marked Henry Greathead down as a professional failure, there is in retrospect no doubting the personal success which he had achieved in the development and propagation of the "Life-Boat". Into a favourable social framework of humanitarian ideals, maritime awareness and upper-class 'interests' he placed not only the instrument, but also the individual commitment, needed to translate other men's good intentions into practical achievements.

Beyond the immediate locality of South Shields and the adjacent 'coble coast' his lifeboats achieved little more than limited acceptance, though their example raised public awareness of the need for lifesaving services and, quite significantly, this did much to spur on others in the field. In their original environment, at the mouth of the Tyne, the Greathead-built boats soon gained a well-deserved reputation for successful lifesaving and safety in operation. This laid the foundations for a tradition of local control, together with the continued usage of Greathead-type boats, which remained long after lifeboat activities elsewhere had merged administratively and technically into a National lifeboat service (the R.N.L.I.).

It seems paradoxical then that Henry Greathead's own reputation fell so rapidly in the town of South Shields itself, to be replaced during the Victorian era with a popular and little contested misconception that Willie Wouldhave had been the true and unrewarded "inventor" of the lifeboat. A variety of social and cultural factors continued to feed this story, even though two prominent local citizen-historians, Thomas Salmon (1856) and George Hodgson (1903), showed a decidedly ambivalent attitude towards it. And, sadly, this rather sterile argument over the "invention of the lifeboat" came to overshadow and parochialise a very real technical and humanitarian achievement.

The town of late eighteenth century South Shields had in fact seen the origination, if not the "invention", of what can now be recognised as the first, purpose-built lifesaving boat to achieve general acceptance and practical success. Its genesis however could not, and cannot, be ascribed solely to any one individual, nor indeed even to the local committee which commissioned the *Original*. From many individuals' reactions within the growing humanitarianism of the age came a desire to save life from shipwreck; from the seafaring experiences of several and, perhaps, through the ingenuity of one came ideas which could be moulded towards a practical design. From the profits of the Coal Trade came the money to finance the project and, eventually, through the receptive mind and skilled hands of a boatbuilder came that functional shell of wood, metal and cordage which could fulfil the final aim.

Finally, however, it is well to remember that all these things would have been of little avail without the sheer guts and broken-water seamanship of that generation of local men who were prepared — for the reward of just a guinea — to risk their own lives for those of others.

Source List

Introduction

1. Davis, R., *The Rise of the English Shipping Industry in the Seventeenth and Eighteenth Centuries* (London, 1962), 35.
2. *Newcastle Courant*, 12 January 1788.
3. Hutchinson, W., *Treatise on Practical Seamanship*, 2nd edition (Liverpool, 1787).
4. Greathead, H., *The Report of the Evidence, and other Proceedings in Parliament respecting the Invention of the Life-Boat* etc. (London, 1804).
5. Whitaker, B., *Skuetender Lifeboat* (South Shields, 1979), 77-88.
6. *Report of The Committee Appointed to Examine the Lifeboat Models submitted to Compete for the Premium offered by His Grace the Duke of Northumberland* (London, 1851).

Chapter One

1. Ville, S., *James Kirton, Shipping Agent*, in *Mariner's Mirror*, Vol. 67, 1981.
2. *Gentleman's Magazine*, September 1806.
3. Welford, R., *Men of Mark 'twixt Tyne and Tweed*, Vol. II (London, 1895), 381-84.
4. *A History of Northumberland*, Vol. I (Newcastle, 1893), 168.
5. N.R.O. 452/C3/39.
6. *Ibid.*
7. Hague, D. B. and Christie, R., *Lighthouses* (Llandysul, 1975), 81.
8. Robus, F., *Lionel Lukin of Dunmow, the Inventor of the Lifeboat* (Dunmow, 1925).
9. N.R.O. 452/C3/49.
10. *Ibid.*
11. *Ibid.*
12. *Ibid.*

13. *Ibid.*
14. Lukin, L., *The Invention, Principles of Construction and uses of Unimmergible Boats* (London, 1806), 33.
15. N.R.O. 452/C3/50.
16. Steel, D., *New Seaman's Guide and Coaster's Companion*, 13th edition (London, 1802).
17. Yorke, B. and R., *Britain's First Lifeboat Station*, (Liverpool, 1982).
18. Hutchinson, 240.
19. Yorke, 19-23.
20. Hutchinson.
21. Lukin, 26.
22. Hutchinson, 262.

Chapter Two

1. *Newcastle Courant*, 21 March 1789.
2. T.W.A.S. 1253/1 (1787/44).
3. *Newcastle Advertiser*, 21 March 1789.
4. Greathead, 24.
5. *Newcastle Courant*, 15 March 1789.
6. *Newcastle Courant*, 9 February, 16 February 1788.
7. in *Tyne Mercury*, 17 August 1802.
8. S.T.L. Lawe House memorabilia.
9. *Newcastle Journal*, 30 June 1832.
10. T.W.A.S. 1253/1.
11. Hodgson, G.B., *The Borough of South Shields from the Earliest Period to the Close of the Nineteenth Century* (Newcastle, 1903).
12. Hails, W.A., *An Enquiry Concerning the Invention of the Life Boat* etc. (Gateshead, 1806), 54.
13. Surtees, R., *The History and Antiquities of the County Palatine of Durham*, Vol. II. (London, 1820), 96.
14. Hails, 54.
15. *Tyne Mercury*, 17 August 1802.
16. Hails, 58.
17. Hails, 54.
18. *Ibid.*

Chapter Three

1. *Public Characters of 1806* (London, 1806), 186-193.
2. Richardson, W., *A Mariner of England* (London, 1970 reprint).
3. *Newcastle Journal*, 20 March 1778.
4. P.R.O. ADM 51/872 (hereafter P.R.O. not cited).
5. ADM 36/8379.
6. Tilley, J.A., *The British Navy and the American Revolution* (South Carolina, 1987).
7. ADM 51/872.
8. *Ibid.*
9. ADM 36/9053.
10. ADM 1/486.
11. ADM 51/1044.
12. *Ibid.*
13. Rawson, G., *The Case of H.M.S. Vulture* in *Mariner's Mirror*, Vol. 35, 1949.
14. *Public Characters of 1806*.
15. Laird Clowes, W., *The Royal Navy* (Boston, 1897-1903) 71-72.
16. ADM 51/1044.
17. Lewis, M., *A Social History of the Navy, 1793-1815* (London, 1960), 294-95.
18. ADM 36/9057.

Chapter Four

1. Hails, 57.
2. *Ibid.*, 58.
3. Welford, Vol.
4. *Tyne Mercury*, 17 August 1802.
5. Hails, 29.
6. *Ibid.* 58-59.
7. *Ibid.* 58.
8. *Ibid.* 55.
9. *Ibid.* 56.
10. Hill, H.O. (Ed. McKee, E.), *The English Coble* (London, 1978).
11. Hutchinson, 1794.

12. Hails, 24-25.
13. Chapelle, H.I., *American Small Sailing Craft* (New York, 1951).
14. Gardner, J., Mystic Seaport Museum, personal communication.
15. Hillhouse & Co., plan collection, 1806, folios 17 and 19, Science Museum, London.
16. D.N.E.O. Y.40a, 9 February 1798.
17. Falconer W., *A New Universal Dictionary of The Marine*, enlarged edition (London, 1815).
18. in Robus, 13-14.
19. N.R.O. ZSW 622/3, 2 April 1798.
20. King, *Notes on Shields and District No. 2, Willie Wouldhave's Birthplace*, Newcastle Central Library.
21. in Hodgson, 487-88.
22. *Ibid.* 428.
23. D.N.E.O. Y.40a, 9 February 1798.
24. *Ibid.*
25. Greathead, 28-29.
26. in *Tyne Mercury*, 17 August 1802.

Chapter Five

1. *Newcastle Courant*, 6 February 1790.
2. Whitaker, 9-14.
3. *Newcastle Courant*, 23 December 1797.
4. Whitaker, 15.
5. D.N.E.O. Y.40a, 9 February 1798.
6. *Ibid.*
7. *Ibid.* 24 September 1798.
8. N.R.O. ZSW 622/3, 2 April 1798.
9. ADM 51/1044.
10. Whitaker, 21-73.
11. N.R.O. ZSW 622/3, 2 April 1798.
12. T.W.C.A.S. 659/427.
13. in *Tracts on The Life Boat*, Newcastle Central Library, 57.

Chapter Six

1. Brockie, W., *Sunderland Notables* (Sunderland, 1894).
2. *Newcastle Courant*, 6 January 1788.
3. N.R.O. ZSW 622/10.
4. Gilligan, H.A., *Captain William Hutchinson and the Early Dublin Bay Lifeboats*, proceedings of the Old Dublin Society, January, 1979.
5. D.N.E.O. 487 F/152, 10 February 1801.
6. *Reports, Papers and Catalogues of the Literary and Philosophical Society, Newcastle upon Tyne, 1799-1802 (Vol. II), 9th Year's Report, 1802*, 5.
7. Brockie, W., *History of the Town of South Shields* etc. (North Shields, 1851), 99-102.
8. N.R.O. ZSW 622/12, 21 October 1801.
9. Greathead, 32-33.
10. Hails, 56.
11. N.R.O. ZSW 622/13, 17 November 1801.
12. Malster, R., *Suffolk Lifeboats – The First Quarter Century*, in *Mariner's Mirror*, Vol. 55, 1969.
13. N.R.O. ZSW 622/14, 16 December 1801.
14. Greathead, 4-5.
15. N.R.O. ZSW 622/3, 2 April 1798.
16. Greathead, 43.
17. Wright, C. and Fayle, C.E., *A History of Lloyd's* (London, 1928), 225.
18. Hodgson, 458.
19. Strachan, J., *A History of Northumbrian Masonry* (London, 1898).
20. Farr, G., *Lists of British Lifeboats, Part I* (Bristol, 1983, for Lifeboat Enthusiasts Society).
21. *Newcastle Courant*, 4 September 1802.
22. *Admiralty Inquiry into Shipbuilding*, 1805.
23. Balmer, R., Ms. *Summary of Newcastle Shipping Registers, 1796-1806*, Tyne and Wear Museums.
24. ADM 106/2244, 16 July 1808.
25. May, W.E. Cdr., *The Boats of Men of War* (London, 1974), 16.
26. ADM 106/2245, 23 November 1808.
27. N.R.O. ZSW 622/20, 12 September 1802.
28. N.R.O. ZSW 622/21, 28 October 1802.
29. McGowan, A., *The Ship: The Century Before Steam, 1700-1820* (London, 1980), 19.
30. *A Collection of Papers on Naval Architecture, European Magazine* (London, 1791), II, vii.
31. *Newcastle Courant*, 1 April 1809.
32. *Newcastle Courant*, 3 November 1810.
33. Surtees, 96.
34. MacKenzie E. and Ross M., *View of the County Palatine of Durham, etc.* (Newcastle, 1834), 52.
35. *Newcastle Courant*, 19 March 1814.
36. *Naval Chronicle*, Vol. 37, 1817, 48-49.

Abbreviations Used:

P.R.O.	Public Record Office
T.W.C.A.S.	Tyne and Wear County Archives Service
N.R.O.	Northumberland Record Office
D.N.E.O.	Duke of Northumberland's Estates Office, archival collections
S.T.L.	South Tyneside Library.

APPENDIX - List of Greathead-type Lifeboats

Year	Builder's Number	Institution	Length & Breadth (Oars) "Name"
1789	1	Local Committee	28′ × 9′4″ (10) "ORIGINAL"
1798	2	Local Committee 1840 − Tyne Lifeboat Institution	30′ × 10′ (10) "NORTHUMBERLAND"
1800	3		
1800	4	Local Committee	
1800	5	Local Committee	
1801	6	Lowestoft Lifeboat Society	30′ × 10′6″ (10)
1801	7	Local Committee 1806 − Suffolk Humane Society	30′ × 10′6″ (10)
1802	8	Ramsgate Harbour Trust	31′ × 10′6″
1802	9		
1802	10	Local Committee	(10)
1802	11	Local Committee 1802 − 23 Tyne Lifeboat Society 1823 − 57 RNLI 1857 − 60 Local Committee 1860 − 80	31′ × 10′6″ (10) "ZETLAND"
1802	12	Crewe Trustees	31′ × 10′6″ (10)
1802	13	Local Committee	"ATHOLL"

Donors/orderers (cost)	Stations	Disposal
Committee of Trade, Port of Newcastle (£150)	South Shields, 1790 – 1830	Wrecked (S) 19.1.1830
2nd Duke of Northumberland (£160)	North Shields, 1798 – c1846	Damaged and Sold
Duke of Northumberland	Lisbon	
Cathcart Dempster and Lloyds	St. Andrews, 1800 – c24	Damaged 1823 broken up
Local Collections and Lloyds	Montrose, 1800 – 34	
Local Collections and Lloyds (Lieut. Wm. Clarke, RN) (£165)	Lowestoft, 1801 – 02 Gorleston, 1802 – 07	Sold 1807
Local Collections and Lloyds (Rev. Dr. Rd. Frank)	Bawdsey Haven, 1801 – 25 Woodbridge Haven, 1825 – 35	
Trust purchase	Ramsgate, 1802 – c24	
Rt. Johnson, Esq., Memel	Memel	
Local Collections and Lloyds (Fras. Gibson) (£160)	Whitby West, 1802 – 17	Unserviceable 1817
Lord Dundas; Rev. Thos. Pym Williamson, etc. (£200)	Redcar, 1802 – 80	Preserved locally
Crewe Trustees	Holy Island, 1802 – 30 North Sunderland, 1830 – 38	Possibly at Bamburgh
Duke of Atholl (£200)	Douglas, 1803 – 14	Broke From moorings, wrecked Dec. 1814

List of Greathead-type Lifeboats Continued.

Year	Builders Number	Institution	Length & Breadth (Oars)
1802	14	Local Committee	30′ × 8′9″ (10)
1802	15	Ayr Harbour Trust	(10)
1802	16	Liverpool Corporation	
1802	17	Local Committee	
1803	18	Royal States of Guernsey	(10)
1803	19	Local Committee	22′ (8)
1803	20	Local Committee	
1803	21	Local Committee	25′ × 9′ (10)
1803	22		
1803	23	Local Committee	27′ × 10′ (10)
1803	24		
1803	25	Local Committee	
1803	26	Local Committee	27′ × 10′ (8)
1803	27		
1803	28		

Donors/Orderers (Cost)	Stations	Disposal
Alexander Baxter	Aberdeen, 1802 – 20	Wrecked (S) March 1820
Provost Geo. Charles and Royal Artillery Co. of Ayr	Ayr, 1803 – c19	
Liverpool Docks Commissioners	Hoylake, 1803 – 10	Wrecked (S) 29.12.1810
Hon. Geo. Rose and Lloyds	Christchurch, 1802 – c25	
State Funds (£170)	Guernsey, 1803 – ?	Rotted away
John Godlee, W. B. Langridge and Lloyds	Newhaven, 1803 – 09 Brighton, 1809 – c16	Rotted away
Philip Langmaid, MP	Plymouth, 1803 – c24	Rotted away
Local subscriptions and Lloyds (Wm. Mill) (£120)	Arbroath, 1803 – 66	Too heavy, worn out
Capt. T. Driver for Merchants	Pillau (now Baltiysk, Lithuania)	
Lord Rolle and Lloyds (£150)	Exmouth, 1803 – c15	
Emperor of Russia	Cronstadt	
Edward Chatterton and Lloyds	Rye, 1803 – c25	
Rd. Oxnam and Lloyds (£150)	Penzance, 1803 – 12	Sold 1812
Prince Royal of Denmark	Elsinore	
Prince Royal of Denmark	Copenhagen	

List of Greathead-type Lifeboats Continued.

Year	Builders Number	Institution	Length & Breadth (Oars)
1803	29	Harbour Trust	28′ × 10′ (12)
1803	30		
1803	31		
1804		Local Committee 1823 Norfolk Association	25′ × 8′6″ (10)
1805		Local Committee 1827 – Lincolnshire Coast Shipwreck Association	30′ × 10′ (12)
1805		Local Committee	
1805			
1805			
1806			
1806		Local Committee	
1807		Town Council (Harbour Lights Committee) 1818 – Harbour Trust	
1808		Harbour Authorities	
1808		Ridley Estate Trust Trustees	30′ (10)
1808		Royal Navy	25′
1810		Trinity House of Kingston – upon – Hull	(10)
1810			

Donors/Orderers (Cost)	Stations	Disposal
Whitehaven Harbour Trust	Whitehaven, 1803 – c23	
King of Prussia	Stettin (Szczecin, Poland)	
Sir Charles Bagge	Gothenburg	
Norwich Mariners' Association	Cromer, 1805 – 30 Wells, 1830 – 51	
Local Subscriptions and Lloyds (£150)	Bridlington, 1805 – 24 Saltfleet, 1827 – 29 Donna Nook, 1829 – 30	Unserviceable 1830
Local Subsriptions and Lloyds	Newhaven (Leith), 1805 – c25	
Honourable East India Company	(Bengal)	
United States Government	(United States)	
The King of Sweden	(Sweden)	
Sir William Forbes	Fraserburgh 1806 – 31	
Local Subscriptions and Lloyds (£130 + £50?)	Montrose, 1807 – 34	
(£372)	Dunbar, 1808 – 21	Unfit, sold 1821
Sir Matthew Ridley and Lloyds	Blyth, 1808 – 10	Wrecked (S) 31.3.1810
Admiralty (five of, £170 each)		
Public Subscription and Lloyds (£200)	Spurn Point, 1810 – 23	Broke adrift, wrecked 8.12.1823
H.M. Government	Heligoland	

List of Greathead-type Lifeboats

The list of Greathead-built lifeboats is, with some additions by the present author, essentially that presented in the *Lists of British Lifeboats, Part One* (1983), compiled by the late Grahame Farr for the Lifeboat Enthusiasts Society, and is presented here with all due acknowledgement to that work.

A full appraisal of the use of Greathead-built boats is beyond the scope of this book. However, it is difficult to disagree with Grahame Farr's informed opinion (in *William Plenty's Lifeboats, 1817-29;* 1975) that, although "...the North Country type, descended from the Greathead boat, had the merit of being well proven in the hands of fishermen crews ... it was disliked almost everywhere outside its own milieu ...". Particular objections to the Greathead-type concerned its weight and level of manning, both of which were considered as too great for the smaller stations.

Wherever success was achieved outwith Tyneside (as at Scarborough, Whitby, Redcar and Sunderland) there was either familiarity with beach-launched cobles or (as at Aberdeen, Dublin and Spurn Point) there was a large experienced body of pilots or longshoremen and an active harbour authority. Elsewhere, after initial trials and successful services – as at St. Andrews and Bawdsey – lack of organisation, finance and maintenance caused the boats to fall into disuse. In a few instances a lack of confidence or of manning seems to have resulted in boats never being used at all; with Penzance, Guernsey and, surprisingly, in view of later achievements, the Isle of Man, falling into this category. More nobly, though, a few boats were lost through well-established active service [(S) in table above.]. Regrettably, the usage, if any, of those boats sent abroad largely remains a mystery.

Although the subsequent development of the North Country-type lifeboat cannot be discussed here, mention should be made of the boats built directly to Greathead's design by: Wake of Sunderland (1800); Smith of Scarborough (1801); Clements of Dublin (1801-1818); Hunter of Hartlepool; and, most interesting of all, those built in Holland under the direction of A. A. Titsingh of the Dutch East India Company (c. 1808).

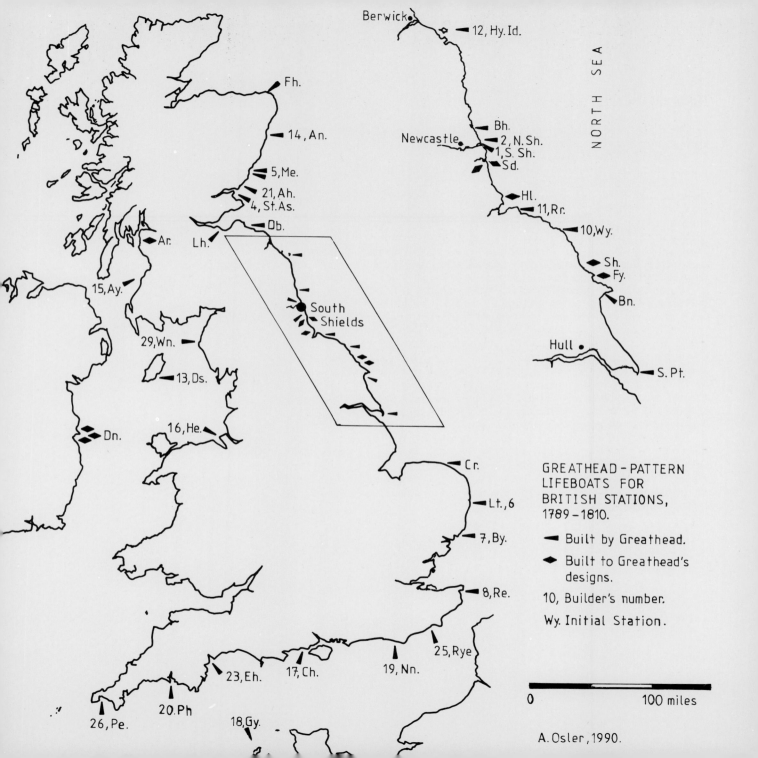

GREATHEAD - PATTERN
LIFEBOATS FOR
BRITISH STATIONS,
1789 - 1810.

◄ Built by Greathead.

◆ Built to Greathead's
designs.

10, Builder's number.

Wy. Initial Station.

0   100 miles

A. Osler, 1990.

References

Bruce G., *Wrecks and Reminiscences of St. Andrew's Bay etc.* (Dundee, 1884).

Malster R. W., *Saved from the Sea* (Lavenham, 1974).

Biggs, H., *The Sound of Maroons* (Lavenham, 1977).

Humble A. F., *The Rowing Lifeboats of Whitby* (Whitby, 1974).

Farr G., *The Early Manx Lifeboats* (Bristol, 1982).

Duthie J. L., *To The Rescue, Lifesaving at Aberdeen, 1802-1924* (Aberdeen)

Sussex Advertiser, 16 May, 1802.

Blampied G., *Mayday! Mayday! A History of the Guernsey Lifeboat Station* (Guernsey, 1984), 10.

Morris and Hendy, *The Story of Newhaven Lifeboats* (n.d.).

Parry J. B., *Historical and Descriptive Account of the Sussex Coast* (1883), 187-88.

Corin J., and Farr G., *Penlee Lifeboat* (Penzance, 1983).

Noalls C., and Farr, G. *Wreck and Rescue Round the Cornish Coast, Vol. II,* 106-09

Whitehaven Gazette, 30th April 1821, 28th October, 1822.

Malster R., and Stibbons P., *The Cromer Lifeboats* (North Walsham, 1979).

Holden C. C., *The History of all Cromer Lifeboats* (unpublished typescript, C. C. Holden Collection, Cromer Museum)

Montrose Directory Almanac, c.1940, 23.

Story A., *Trinity House of Kingston upon Hull* (Grimsby), 96-103.

de Courcy Ireland, J., *Wreck and Rescue on the East Coast of Ireland* (Dublin, 1983).

de Courcy Ireland, J., *Safety in the Approaches to the Port of Dublin*, in Mariners Mirror, Vol. 72, 1986.

Morris J., *The Story of the Hoylake and West Kirby Lifeboats* (Coventry, 1985), 1-3

de Booy H. Th., in *De Reddingboot*, no. 101, 1966, 4245-4251.

Alle hens gered (Rotterdam, 'Prins Hendrik' Maritiem Museum, 1968), 12-15, 40-41.

Sources of Illustrations

The Tyne and Wear County Museums Service particularly acknowledges the permission given by the National Maritime Museum to photograph, for purposes of illustration in this book, the models shown in Chapter Six, figs. 2 and 7; together with permission to reproduce other items as listed.

Especial acknowledgement is also given to the Newcastle Central Library, South Shields Library, Tyne and Wear County Archives Service, and Northumberland County Record Office for providing the facility to copy and reproduce material as listed.

Permission to depict or reproduce individual items from the collections of the Statens Sjohistoriska Musuem (Stockholm), the Literary and Philosophical Society of Newcastle upon Tyne and the Rotunda Museum (Scarborough) is also gratefully acknowledged.

Abbreviations used:

N.C.L.	Newcastle Central Library.
N.C.R.O.	Northumberland County Record Office.
S.T.L.	South Tyneside Library.
T.W.A.S.	Tyne and Wear Archives Service.
N.M.M.	National Maritime Museum.
T.W.C.M.S.	Tyne and Wear County Museums Service (S.S., South Shields Museum; M.S.&E., Museum of Science and Engineering, Newcastle; L.A.G., Laing Art Gallery, Newcastle).

Cover and Endpapers

T.W.C.M.S. (L.A.G.), T.W.C.M.S. (M.S.&E.)

Introduction

1. N.C.L.
2. T.W.C.M.S. (M.S.&E.)
3. T.W.C.M.S. (L.A.G.)
4. N.C.L.

Chapter One

1. N.C.R.O. (by permission of the Trustees of Lord Crewe's Charity)
2. N.C.L.
3. T.W.C.M.S. (L.A.G.)
4. T.W.C.M.S. (M.S.&E.)
5. S.T.L.
6. N.C.L.

Chapter Two

1. Private Collection
2. T.W.C.M.S. (M.S.&E.)
3. T.W.A.S.
4. T.W.C.M.S. (S.S.)
5. S.T.L.
6. T.W.C.M.S. (M.S.&E.)
7. N.C.L.

Chapter Three

1. N.M.M.
2. T.W.C.M.S. (M.S.&E.)
3., 4. N.M.M.
5. T.W.C.M.S. (M.S.&E.)

Chapter Four

1., 2. T.W.C.M.S. (S.S.)
3. N.M.M.
4., 5., 6., 7. T.W.C.M.S. (M.S.&E.)
8. Statens Sjohistoriska Museum, Stockholm.
9. T.W.C.M.S. (S.S.)

Chapter Five

1. Private Collection
2., 3. T.W.C.M.S. (M.S.&E.)
4. N.C.L.
5. S.T.L.
6. T.W.C.M.S. (S.S.)
7. T.W.A.S.

Chapter Six

1. N.C.L. (Henry Greathead), Newcastle Literary and Philosophical Society (Sir John Swinburne), N.C.L. (Rowland Burdon, M.P.), N.C.L. (Hugh, Earl Percy, second Duke of Northumberland)
2. N.M.M.
3. N.C.L.
4. Scarborough Borough Council
5. T.W.C.M.S. (M.S.&E.)
6. T.W.C.M.S. (S.S.)
7. N.M.M.

Illi robur et æs triplex
 Circa pectus erat, qui fragilem truci
Commisit pelago ratem
 primus,

                              Hor.

Oak and triple bronze were about his breast,
who first committed his fragile ship to the
 savage sea.

                              Horace Odes I.3 Lines 9-12

These few lines of Horace (65-8 BC), taken from a "sending off" poem (*propempticon*) for Virgil,
were used by Dr Trotter, Physician to the British Fleet, as a preface to a laudatory ode addressed to
Greathead in 1801.

 Horace employs a striking metaphor, referring to characteristic features of contemporary war
galleys, not present in merchant vessels, in order to emphasize the bravery of the first man to put
to sea. The *oak* is the keel of the galley, which had to be robust to withstand frequent hauling out.
The *triple bronze* is the three pronged ram which formed its armoured prow.

 The sea's timeless challenge makes Greathead's skill and the courage of the first Shield's lifeboat
crew equally worthy of emphasis.